Medical Teeline

Other Teeline titles available

Teeline: Revised Edition by I.C. Hill and Meriel Bowers
Teeline Revised Edition: Teacher's Guide by Meriel Bowers
Teeline Fast by Ann Dix
Teeline Shorthand Made Simple by Harry Butler
First Teeline Workbook: Revised Edition by I.C. Hill and Meriel Bowers
Second Teeline Workbook Revised Edition by I.C. Hill and Meriel
Bowers
Teeline Word List by I.C. Hill
Teeline Word Groupings by George Hill
New Teeline Dictation Book edited by George Hill
Teeline Shorthand Dictation Passages by Dorothy Bower
Handbook for Teeline Teachers edited by Harry Butler

Medical Teeline

PAT GARNER & PAT CLARE

HEINEMANN
EDUCATIONAL

Heinemann Educational Books Ltd
Halley Court, Jordan Hill, Oxford OX2 8EJ

OXFORD LONDON EDINBURGH MADRID
ATHENS BOLOGNA PARIS MELBOURNE
SYDNEY AUCKLAND SINGAPORE TOKYO
IBADAN NAIROBI HARARE GABORONE
PORTSMOUTH NH (USA)

Text © Pat Garner and Pat Clare 1987
Teeline outlines © Teeline Education Ltd 1987
First published 1987
94 95 13 12 11 10 9 8 7 6 5

British Library Cataloguing in Publication Data

Garner, Pat
    Medical Teeline.
    1. Medical shorthand   2. Shorthand—
    Teeline
    I. Title   II. Clare, Pat
    653'.428   R728.8

    ISBN 0–435–45315–7

All persons referred to in the case studies are wholly invented, and
any similarity to any persons now living is unintended and entirely
coincidental.

Printed in Great Britain by Athenaeum Press Ltd, Newcastle

Contents

1 Introducing Medical Teeline

Your introduction to medical Teeline can take place while you are learning Teeline theory. For the most part, this chapter relates to the theory given in the textbook *Teeline: Revised Edition*. However, because of the complexity of medical words, and the need to shorten outlines, a limited amount of alternative theory, which is considered to be particularly relevant to medical Teeline, has been introduced. Once you have learned the theory, in certain instances you may find it useful to devise 'short cuts'. In this book some very long outlines have been shortened so that they may be written more quickly. Medical secretaries working in specialities in hospitals generally find their own ways of shortening outlines.

This chapter contains medical terms relevant to Teeline theory, and asks you to write sentences including these terms. In addition, half-way through the chapter there is some simple medical dictation material. If you do not know the meaning of all the words used, look them up in a medical dictionary.

MEDICAL WORDS TO PRACTISE AFTER UNIT 4

Letters S, T and D

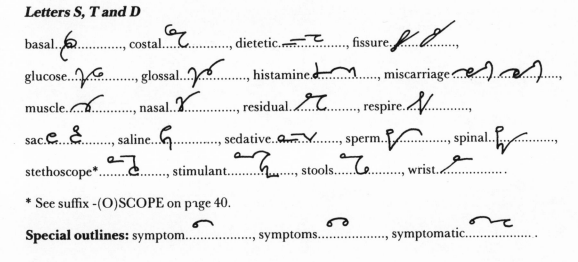

basal..........., costal..........., dietetic..........., fissure...........,

glucose..........., glossal..........., histamine..........., miscarriage...........,

muscle..........., nasal..........., residual..........., respire...........,

sac..........., saline..........., sedative..........., sperm..........., spinal...........,

stethoscope*..........., stimulant..........., stools..........., wrist...........,

* See suffix -(O)SCOPE on page 40.

Special outlines: symptom..............., symptoms..............., symptomatic................ .

Circle B

In Unit 4 students are introduced to circle B representing the word *be*. Consonant B, when attached to certain letters, can also be represented by a large circle. This is especially helpful in shortening medical outlines.

DB......, BD......, TB......, BT......, BL......, MB......, BM......, PB......, BP......,

BW......, WB......, HB......, BH......

Note: LB should not be shown with a circle B because it can easily be mistaken as letter B.

blast........, bowed........, debilitate........, metabolism........,

mobile........, swabs........, tablets........, webbed........ .

Circle B (on its own) can also represent the commonly used word *blood*, i.e.

blood pressure........ *or* ...., blood sugar........ *or* ....

Medical terms that are commonly used can also be shown by their initials (see page 61).

Put the following sentences into Teeline:

1   You will soon need to get some histamine tablets.
2   The woman's blood pressure was very high.
3   The man was mobile despite the accident.
4   He will need to take a specimen stool to the lab.
5   He took the tablets to stimulate his metabolism.

MEDICAL WORDS TO PRACTISE AFTER UNIT 5

A, Y and I endings

Teeline: Revised Edition states that a full 'A' should be used at the end of P, H and M. It is also easier to write a full A at the end of N.

biopsy........, costa........, patella........, rubella........,

saliva........, sanity........, sciatica........, sigmoidostomy........,

spina bifida........, systole........, thigh........, tuberosity........ .

In *Teeline: Revised Edition* the Y can be used to represent OY in the middle and at the end of words. In medical terminology, the Y followed by D may be used for the ending -OID, e.g.

mastoid........, rheumatoid........, sarcoid........ .

Special outlines: clinic........, clinical........, clinically........,

surgery........ .

A and E beginnings

adipose........, angina........, anus........, apathy........,

earache........, enema........, enzyme........, epidemic........,

epilepsy........, erupted........, oedema........, oesophagus........ .

Special outlines: abnormal........, normal........, ambulance........

I and O beginnings

eyelid..⟨shorthand⟩.........., eye-teeth.....⟨shorthand⟩.........., iliac region..⟨shorthand⟩......, illegitimate..⟨shorthand⟩...........,

immune..⟨shorthand⟩.........., impetigo..⟨shorthand⟩..........., injury..⟨shorthand⟩........., innate...............,

inoculate..⟨shorthand⟩.........., inquest..⟨shorthand⟩..........., *in situ*..⟨shorthand⟩..........., iris..⟨shorthand⟩.........,

oculist...⟨shorthand⟩.........., opaque..⟨shorthand⟩.............., ophthalmic..⟨shorthand⟩......., optic..⟨shorthand⟩...........,

os..⟨shorthand⟩............. .

Distinguishing outlines: ileum...⟨shorthand⟩........., ilium...⟨shorthand⟩......... .

U beginnings and endings

residue..⟨shorthand⟩.........., tissue................, ulna..⟨shorthand⟩..........., ultimate..⟨shorthand⟩........,

umbilical..⟨shorthand⟩......., unit................. .

Put the following sentences into Teeline:

1 A biopsy may reveal any abnormal cells.
2 The woman needed a sedative to settle her nerves.
3 A stethoscope may be used to listen to the chest.
4 She was advised to have a spinal corset for her back injury.
5 He needed surgery to repair the damage to his elbow.

MEDICAL WORDS TO PRACTISE AFTER UNIT 6

'S(C) vowel S' endings

In medical terminology, the frequency of 'S(C) vowel S' at the end of words is very high. It is quite safe to use a disjoined S to represent most of these endings, e.g.

abscess..⟨shorthand⟩.........., analysis...⟨shorthand⟩............., illnesses...⟨shorthand⟩..........., sepsis..⟨shorthand⟩.............,

stasis................, uresis..⟨shorthand⟩............. .

However, it is necessary to distinguish between the singular ending -SIS and its plural -SES as follows:

analysis..⟨shorthand⟩............., analyses..⟨shorthand⟩............. .

The ending -OSIS is represented by a disjoined O indicator with an S, e.g.

osmosis..⟨shorthand⟩......... .

Special outlines: diagnosis..⟨shorthand⟩..........., diagnoses..⟨shorthand⟩........... .

-ING, INGLE, -NCE, and -NCH

assessing............., balance............., bunch............., clotting.............,

finger............., imbalance............., impotence............., pinched.............,

shadowing............., shingles............., sublingual............. .

Put the following sentences into Teeline:

1   The woman pinched her finger in the machine.
2   An analysis of the data showed that she had a hormone imbalance.
3   The tablets had to be used sublingually.
4   The diagnosis showed that the woman had shingles.
5   The shingles and varicella viruses are related.

MEDICAL WORDS TO PRACTISE AFTER UNIT 7

Note: The prefixes ANTA-, ANTE-, and ANTI- can be shown by disjoined AN in the T position (see *Second Teeline Workbook: Revised Edition*, page 20), e.g.

antenatal............., antibiotic............., antigen............. .

T and D beginnings

dialysis............., diastolic............., digestive............., digit.............,

dosage............., douche............., duct............., tepid.............,

testicle............., thiamine............., topical............., twitch............. .

Distinguishing outlines: tubal............., tubule............. .

Special outlines: disease............., diseases............., discharge(d)............. .

T and D in the middle and at the end of words

atypical............., botulism............., buttocks............., diabetes.............,

intubate............., ketosis............., libido............., metabolic.............,

obesity............. .

Special outlines: abdomen............., abdominal............. .

Put the following sentences into Teeline:

1 Antibiotics are used for a vast number of illnesses.
2 The man with fatigue was diagnosed as having diabetes.
3 There was a discharge from the abscess.
4 The woman had loss of libido as well as epilepsy.
5 The girl was advised to go to the antenatal clinic for tests.

MEDICAL WORDS TO PRACTISE AFTER UNIT 8

Letters F and L

effective. ......, faint. ......, fatal ......, fever ......, focus ......,

foetus ......, fundus ......, hilum ......, labour ......,

lanolin ......, laparoscopy* ......, lavage ......, lens ......,

lethal ......, lint ......, malignant ......, palsy ......,

pelvis ......, pills ......, soporific ......, typhoid ......

* See suffix -(O)SCOPY on page 40.

T and D following R and L

apparatus ......, cardiac ......, carotid ......, cartilage ......,

cured ......, degenerate ......, dilate ......, epiglottis ......,

eroded ......, gliding ......, heart ......, heredity ......,

parotid ......, puberty ......, operating ......, radical ......,

radium ......, serrated ......

Special outline: hospital ......

Put the following sentences into Teeline:

1 Until I see him again, I shall not know if his diabetes has stabilised.
2 The boy was admitted to hospital with a suspected damaged pelvis.
3 Laparoscopy is used to view the abdominal cavity.
4 The fever left the woman when she finished the course of antibiotics.
5 The foetal heart could be heard with the aid of a stethoscope.

MEDICAL WORDS TO PRACTISE AFTER UNIT 9

-MENT

ailments............., alimentary............., elements............., ligament.............,

liniments............., medicament............., ointment............., pigment.............,

sediment............., sentiment............., temperament.............,

malalignment............. .

Special outline: appointment............. .

-TION

abortion............., absorption............., admission............., circulation.............,

dilatation............., dilation............., generation............., gestation.............,

lesion............., ligation............., manipulation............., mastication.............,

medication............., operation............., optician............., physician.............,

remission............., solution............. .

Special outline: patient............. .

Alternatively -TION can be attached to T and D (see *Second Teeline Workbook: Revised Edition*, page 16).

Put the following sentences into Teeline:

1   The man needed medication for his poor circulation.
2   The optician sent the patient to see an ophthalmic surgeon.
3   The patient requested an appointment with the physician.
4   Using both ointment and liniment eased the ligament pain.
5   The man's cartilage in his knee was causing him so much pain that he needed an operation.

MEDICAL WORDS TO PRACTISE AFTER UNIT 10

F blends

acephalous............., diaphragm............., Fallopian tube.............,

fertile............., flatulence............., follicle............., formalin.............,

fragment............., frailty............., frequency............., friction............., frozen............., inflamed............., lymph............., midwife.............,

nephritis*............., nephrotomy............., perforation............., phallus.............,

pharmacist............., phlebitis............., referral............., refraction.............,

syphilis............. .

* See suffix -ITIS on page 33.

Special outline: phalanges............. (see *Second Teeline Workbook: Revised Edition*, page 26).

Put the following sentences into Teeline:

1   He had to have fragments of glass removed from his eye.
2   The woman suffering with flatulence collected her pills from the pharmacist.
3   A blockage in the Fallopian tubes caused the woman to be infertile.
4   The man was referred to a local hospital for additional tests.
5   It was suspected that the single man was suffering from AIDS.

MEDICAL WORDS TO PRACTISE AFTER UNIT 11

TR blend

administer............., bilateral............., deterioration............., dysentery.............,

enteritis............., fester............., geriatric............., laboratory.............,

menstruation............., metatarsals............., mitral............., nitrogen.............,

nostril............., nutrition............., obstetrics............., oestrogen.............,

parturition............., pituitary............., sterile............., tarsal.............,

terminal............., traction............., trauma............., triceps.............,

trophic............., trypsin............., turgid............. .

Special outlines: temperature............., treatment............. .

THR at the beginning of a word

In most medical words, it is safe to show THR at the beginning of words as ...., with

the exception of the root *thorac* which should be shown as ...., e.g.

theory................., therapeutic............., therapy............., therm................., thermolysis............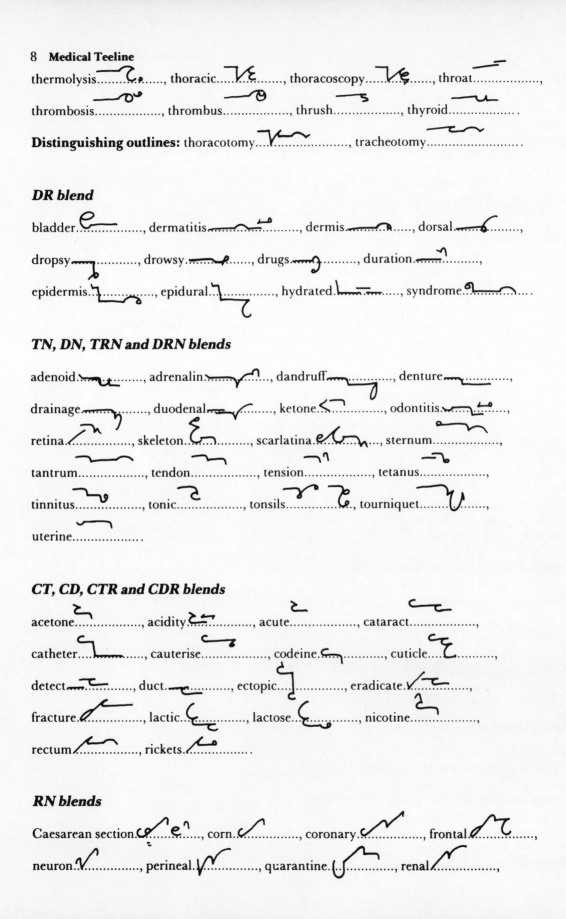......, thoracic..................., thoracoscopy..............., throat.................,

thrombosis..............., thrombus..............., thrush..............., thyroid.................

Distinguishing outlines: thoracotomy..................., tracheotomy.................

DR blend

bladder.................., dermatitis..................., dermis..............., dorsal...............,

dropsy..............., drowsy..............., drugs..............., duration...............,

epidermis..............., epidural..............., hydrated..............., syndrome.............

TN, DN, TRN and DRN blends

adenoid..............., adrenalin..............., dandruff..............., denture...............,

drainage..............., duodenal..............., ketone..............., odontitis...............,

retina..............., skeleton..............., scarlatina..............., sternum...............,

tantrum..............., tendon..............., tension..............., tetanus...............,

tinnitus..............., tonic..............., tonsils..............., tourniquet...............,

uterine...............

CT, CD, CTR and CDR blends

acetone..............., acidity..............., acute..............., cataract...............,

catheter..............., cauterise..............., codeine..............., cuticle...............,

detect..............., duct..............., ectopic..............., eradicate...............,

fracture..............., lactic..............., lactose..............., nicotine...............,

rectum..............., rickets...............

RN blends

Caesarean section..............., corn..............., coronary..............., frontal...............,

neuron..............., perineal..............., quarantine..............., renal..............., rhinitis............, rhinoscopy............, stillborn............, syringe............

Put the following sentences into Teeline:

1 An epidural was used to relieve the woman of pain during labour.
2 The child's adenoids and tonsils appeared inflamed.
3 The elderly man was nearly blind because of the cataracts in his eyes.
4 Oestrogen is used to relieve women of some of the effects of the menopause.
5 The man who had had a coronary thrombosis failed to appear for his appointment.
6 The patient was put on traction following the car accident.

MEDICAL WORDS TO PRACTISE AFTER UNIT 12

LR, MR and WR blends

accelerate............, allergic............, caloric............, chlorine............,

cholera............, femur............, haemorrhage............, haemorrhoids............,

jugular............, lordosis............, mammary............, marrow............

mercury............, morbid............, moron............, morphine............,

mortuary............, murmur............, muscular............, sclerosis............,

threadworm............, tumour............, ward*............, wart.............

* In word groupings *ward* is written as a small 'w' in the D position, i.e. to the ward............
(see page 18).

Distinguishing outlines: vascular............, vesicular............

Put the following sentences into Teeline:

1 The woman needed an operation to remove the mammary tumour.
2 Bone marrow tests were carried out to find the right donor.
3 Muscular dystrophy is a degenerative disease more usually found in boys.
4 A worsening of the lordosis meant that the workman had to leave his job.
5 The *post mortem* revealed that the patient had died from a haemorrhage.

MEDICAL WORDS TO PRACTISE AFTER UNIT 13

Vowel indicators as word endings

fungal............, ganglion............, gangrene............, longevity*............,

lungs............, mongol.............

* Disjoined V in the T position is used for -AVITY, -EVITY, and -IVITY (see *Second Teeline Workbook: Revised Edition*, page 22).

Words ending with a double vowel sound

The double vowel ending should be used for some outlines but, because there are many medical words ending in -IA, in these cases it is sufficient to use the -A ending only.

algesia................, alopecia................, amenorrhoea................, amnesia................,

anaemia................, aphasia................, bacteria................, dyspepsia................,

hernia................, malacia................, malaria................, neuralgia................,

phobia................, pneumonia................, polio................, radius................,

sartorius................, steatorrhoea................ .

Put the following sentences into Teeline:

1   Down's syndrome is another name for mongolism.
2   The young man with malaria had very little strength.
3   The woman suffering from amenorrhoea was infertile.
4   Alopecia is the loss of hair from the head and/or body.
5   The gangrenous leg needed to be amputated.

Prepare the following for dictation:

This young man has had a stubborn rash on his[10] fingers for a long time. There is no evidence of[20] fungal infection, and I believe the rash is eczema. I[30] have told him to take Piriton tablets, one td[40]s, and to use Ultradil at night. He will be[50] returning to the clinic in one month's time.

(*58 words*)

MEDICAL WORDS TO PRACTISE AFTER UNIT 14

Vowel indicators as word endings: -ANK, -INK, -ONK and -UNK

blanket................, canker................, carbuncle................, function................,

linctus................, tincture................, truncate................, trunk................,

zinc................ .

Special outline: ankle................ .

Put the following sentences into Teeline:

1   The drunkard went to the casualty department and demanded immediate attention.
2   The torn ligament in the ankle caused both pain and loss of movement.
3   I think we should operate immediately and obtain a biopsy of the tumour.
4   The baby who had drunk the cough linctus appeared very drowsy.
5   The accident victim in the ambulance was wrapped in a blanket.

MEDICAL WORDS TO PRACTISE AFTER UNIT 15

X blends

anthrax................., antitoxin...................., apex....................,

carbon monoxide..................., cervix...................., coccyx..................., dextrose...................,

dyslexia..............., eczema...................., elixir...................., exacerbate....................,

excision..............., excretion...................., expand...................., expectant....................,

expectorant..............., extensor...................., external...................., extract....................,

extremity..............., larynx...................., laxative...................., myxoedema....................,

oxidation..............., oxygen...................., peroxide...................., phalanx....................,

pharynx..............., pyrexia...................., relax...................., sexual....................,

smallpox..............., thyrotoxicosis...................., thyroxin...................., toxic....................,

waxy................. .

Special outlines: accident..............., X-ray...................... .

Note: The frequently used word *examination* can be shown in word groupings as follows:

on examination..............., your examination...................., further examination....................,

rectal examination................. .

The full X is used in word groupings for *accident* as follows:

your accident..............., further accident.................... .

Put the following sentences into Teeline:

1 An X-ray revealed a fracture of the femur.
2 The child's eczema was treated with topical steroids.
3 A toxic substance in the air had caused the skin irritation.
4 Her reflexes were poor as a result of the sciatica.
5 The man suffering from carbon monoxide poisoning was resuscitated.

Prepare the following for dictation:

I am referring this lady to you for your opinion.[10] She is 55 years of age, and has been[20] exhibiting physical and mental fatigue for approximately 6 months. Just[30] a small amount of exercise leaves her exhausted, and she[40] is experiencing difficulty in keeping warm. Her skin is extremely[50] dry, and she has extensive thinning of hair on her[60] scalp. There is a slow relaxation phase of the deep[70] tendon reflexes which, together with the other symptoms, does indicate[80] the likelihood of her having myxoedema. I should be obliged[90] if you would examine her and, if you confirm my[100] diagnosis, put her on a suitable thyroxine therapy.

(108 words)

MEDICAL WORDS TO PRACTISE AFTER UNIT 16

CM blends

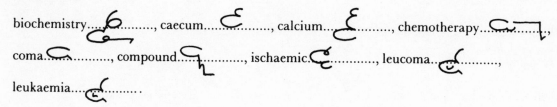

biochemistry.............., caecum.............., calcium.............., chemotherapy..............,

coma.............., compound.............., ischaemic.............., leucoma..............,

leukaemia.............. .

Put the following sentences into Teeline:

1 Chemotherapy may be used in the treatment of leukaemia.
2 She was in a lot of discomfort during the rectal examination.
3 During a routine eye test, the optician diagnosed leucoma.
4 Calcium is needed to form strong bones and teeth.
5 The man was diagnosed as having ischaemic heart disease.

MEDICAL WORDS TO PRACTISE AFTER UNIT 17

N and V blends

evacuation.............., involuntary.............., navel.............., ovary..............,

ovulate.............., synovial.............., unwell.............., valvular..............,

varicose.............., veins.............., venereal.............., ventilation..............,

ventricle.............., verruca.............., vertex.............., vertigo..............,

villi.............., virile.............., virus.............., volume.............., vulva..............,

wean.............., windpipe.............., wounds.............. .

Special outlines: deliver/y/ed.............., develop/ed.............. .

Put the following sentences into Teeline:

1 The man became unwell while driving his delivery van.
2 The varicose veins had caused the woman a lot of discomfort.
3 Some forms of venereal disease are treated with antibiotics.
4 The patient had an involuntary evacuation of the bowels following the enema.
5 An operation was required to repair the heart valves.

Prepare the following for dictation:

I saw this lady in my clinic recently. She has[10] been feeling generally unwell, and in particular has been experiencing[20] pain in her left leg. Five years ago, I operated[30] on her to remove the varicose veins in her right[40] leg, and it would appear that she now requires the[50] same operation on her left leg. Her name has been[60] put on the waiting list and it is hoped that[70] surgery can be performed within the next 6 months.

(79 words)

MEDICAL WORDS TO PRACTISE AFTER UNIT 18

CN blends

blood count............., centrifugal............., conception.............,

concussion............., condyle............., congenital............., congestion.............,

conjunctivitis............., constipation............., contraceptive.............,

contraction............., convalescence............., convulsions.............,

scanner............., secondary.............

Special outlines: cancer............., carcinoma............. The two words are written as large C's unlike the flattened CM blend.

consultant............., contra-indicated.............

Put the following sentences into Teeline:

1 Chemotherapy is used extensively in the treatment of cancer.
2 The foetus showed signs of congenital deformity.
3 The contraceptive pill was given to the woman to regulate her periods.
4 The lung cancer metastasised and secondary tumours arose very rapidly.
5 The consultant was concerned when the patient admitted with mild concussion lapsed into unconsciousness.

Prepare the following for dictation:

This young man came to my surgery today suffering with[10] all the symptoms of concussion. He had collided with another[20] player on the rugby field, after which he had been[30] unconscious for a few minutes. On regaining consciousness he had[40] a severe headache. Later today he started to feel dizzy[50] and was vomiting. He was very concerned about his condition,[60] and I have reassured him that the symptoms are likely[70] to clear within a day or so. However, I think[80] it would be advisable for him to have his head[90] X-rayed so that we can confirm there is no serious[100] damage.

(101 words)

MEDICAL WORDS TO PRACTISE AFTER UNIT 19

P blends

Note: The PL can be lengthened for R, but this must not be used at the beginning of an outline.

complaint............., complication............., implant............., neoplasma.............

nipple............., palate............., palpation............., palsy.............,

pelvis............., piles............., placebo............., placenta............., plasma......., plaster......., plastic......., platelets.......,

pleura......., pleurisy......., puberty......., pubic.......,

pulmonary......., scalpel......., spleen......., splint.......

Put the following sentences into Teeline:

1   The man with piles complained about the pain he was experiencing.
2   The patient had a pulmonary embolism following major surgery.
3   Plastic surgery is often used in the treatment of badly burned patients.
4   Placebos are dummy tablets that are sometimes given to patients.
5   An exploratory examination revealed that the woman had a damaged spleen.

Prepare the following for dictation:

This lady has been complaining of pain in the pelvic[10] region for about 3 months. She has been well in[20] all other respects. On palpation, I could find nothing to[30] indicate the likely cause of her condition, and I have[40] therefore arranged for her to be admitted within the next[50] two months for laparoscopy and further tests.

(57 words)

MEDICAL WORDS TO PRACTISE AFTER UNITS 20 and 21

Word beginnings and full vowels as word endings

compatibility......., curable......., disability......., dribble.......,

flexibility......., immiscible......., irritability......., mandible.......,

operable......., overcompensation......., overdose.......,

overhydration......., stability......., transection.......,

transference......., transfusion......., transplant.......,

transposition........

Put the following sentences into Teeline:

1   The surgeon carried out a lung and heart transplant on the young child.
2   During the examination the consultant surgeon came to the conclusion that the cancer was operable.
3   The road accident victim needed an immediate blood transfusion.
4   The woman had a tendency to overbalance and needed a walking frame to overcome her disability.
5   She was to undergo a rhinoplasty in order to correct a deflected septum.

MEDICAL WORDS TO PRACTISE AFTER UNIT 22

R principle: BR, CR and GR

afebrile............., brachial............., bradycardia............., bromide.............,

bronchi............., bronchitis............., bruise............., cardiac.............,

cartilage............., centigrade............., cerebral............., chronic.............,

cramp............., cranium............., crepitation............., cretin.............,

crisis............., critical............., croup............., endocrine.............,

fibrous............., germicide............., graft............., granular.............,

gravid............., gravity............., groin............., growth.............,

migraine............., scrotum..............

Special outlines: barium............., barium meal............., barium enema..............

Put the following sentences into Teeline:

1   The secretary's migraine gradually worsened as the crisis grew.
2   The graduate with chronic bronchitis became critically ill.
3   The girl with cerebral palsy was sent to a special school.
4   A barium meal was used in an attempt to determine the cause of the woman's stomach pain.
5   The crisis passed and the man was taken off the critical list.

Prepare the following for dictation:

I saw this elderly gentleman 3 weeks ago when he[10] came to the clinic suffering with chronic bronchitis. He complained[20] of central chest pain, and had been coughing up green[30] sputum. The great difficulty in breathing which he was experiencing[40] was causing him considerable distress and he was particularly worried[50] because he has to climb two flights of stairs at[60] least twice a day in order to reach his flat.[70] I decided to admit him to the medical ward for[80] bed rest and observation. He was put on a course[90] of tetracycline which seems to have eased his symptoms. He[100] now appears to be much brighter in himself, and is[110] eating more food. His condition, therefore, is no longer grave.[120] He was discharged from hospital today, and I have advised[130] him to see you in one week's time.

(138 words)

MEDICAL WORDS TO PRACTISE AFTER UNIT 23

R principle: AR, OR, UR and PR

artery............., arrhythmia............., articulate............., artificial.............,

leprosy............., oral............., orchitis............., organic............., practitioner............, pregnancy............, premature............, pressure............,

primary............, primigravida............, probe............, proctalgia............,

prognosis............, prolapse............, prone............, proptosis............,

prostate............, prosthesis............, protrusion............, proud............,

purulent............, ureter............, urethra*............, uric............,

urine............, urticaria............ .

* See prefix URETHR- on page 50.

Special outlines: aorta............, improve/ed/ing............, orthopaedic............,

prescribe/d............, prescription............, problem............,

reproduction............ .

Put the following sentences into Teeline:

1   There was an improvement in her arthritis following administration of hydrocortisone.
2   The premature baby needed urgent medical care.
3   The woman with a prolapsed disc experienced considerable pain in the leg.
4   The doctor's preliminary findings revealed a protein deficiency.
5   The general practitioner prescribed a placebo for the hypochondriac* patient.

* See prefix HYPO- on page 32.

Prepare the following for dictation:

Thank you for referring this lady who presented with abdominal[10] pain and frequency of micturition. She is a primigravida who[20] was delivered 2 months ago of a healthy baby. On[30] examination I discovered that she has a prolapsed uterus which[40] is causing pressure on the bladder. The problem can be[50] resolved by minor surgery, and I have arranged to admit[60] her to the clinic next week.

(66 words)

MEDICAL WORDS TO PRACTISE AFTER UNIT 24

Extensions of PR, Circle B on M, and O on M

chamber............, compress............, depress............, depressant............,

depression............, embolism............, express............, fibroma............,

grumbling............, impregnate............, lumbago............, membrane............, motion............, omphalocele............, remove............, repression............;

vomer............, vomit............ .

Special outlines: inject............, injection............ .

Put the following sentences into Teeline:

1 The child with a grumbling appendix was admitted to the ward.
2 A cold compress was used to relieve the swelling on the leg.
3 Following the operation, the woman suffered severe depression and was prescribed an antidepressant.
4 Hysterectomy is the surgical removal of the womb.
5 The lumbago was becoming a serious problem for the athlete.

MEDICAL WORDS TO PRACTISE AFTER UNITS 25–7

Word beginnings: ENC-, INC-, INS-, and AFTER-

afterbirth............, after-care............, afterpains............, encapsulation............,

encephalitis............, encopresis............, incision............, incoherent............,

incompatible............, incontinent............, incubation............,

insanity............, insemination............, insidious............, insomnia............,

inspiration............, insulin............, intercostal*............ .

* Words beginning with INTER- can be written without the N............ .

Word beginnings: CIRCUM-, ELECTRIC-/ELECTRO-, and MAGNE-

circumcision............, circumduction............, electrolytes............,

electron............, electrotherapy............, magnesium............,

electroconvulsive therapy*............ .

* This medical term is also known by its abbreviation ECT............ .

You can use the abbreviation in your shorthand notes, but insert a line underneath the outline if the term is to be transcribed in full (see page 61), e.g.

CNS............, *or* central nervous system............ .

Word beginnings: MULTI-, NON-, NATION-, SEMI-, SUPER- and UPPER-

multicellular............., multigravida............., multipara.............,

non compos mentis............., non-specific............., non-viable.............,

semicomatose............., seminal............., supercilium.............,

super-ego............., superior............., supernumerary..............

Put the following sentences into Teeline:

1 Patients suffering from depression can benefit from electroconvulsive therapy.
2 Insulin is a vital substance in the treatment of diabetes.
3 For some couples artificial insemination by a donor may be the only way of producing a child.
4 The premature baby was placed in an incubator immediately after delivery.
5 The woman had miscarried the non-viable foetus.

MEDICAL WORDS TO PRACTISE AFTER UNITS 28–30

Word endings: -OLOGY, -GRAPH, -GRAM and -WARD

cardiologist............., cholecystogram............., cytology.............,

gynaecologist............., histological............., neurologist.............,

ophthalmology............., pathological*............., physiological.............,

radiography............., radiologist............., rhinology.............,

ventriculograph............., virology..............

* See prefix PATHO- on page 41.

Special outlines: medical ward............., surgical ward..............

Word endings: -ALITY, -ILITY, -ERITY and -NESS

debility............., dexterity............., fertility............., fragility.............,

infertility............., mobility............., mortality............., sterility.............,

tiredness..............

Special outlines: abnormality............., normality..............

Soft C, AU at beginning of words, and G for J

auditory......................, aural......................, auricle......................, auscultation......................,

induced......................, lice......................, opacity......................, receptor......................,

ulcer......................

Put the following sentences into Teeline:

1   The gynaecologist prescribed tablets to improve the woman's fertility.
2   A cholecystogram revealed that stones were present in the gall-bladder.
3   On auscultation heart murmurs were heard.
4   Her peptic ulcer was treated with antacids.
5   The X-ray revealed pathological fractures indicating malignancy.

LARGE LETTERS

Medical secretaries working in specialities in hospitals often devise ways of shortening outlines of words that they frequently write. The following are examples of how large Teeline letters can be used to represent words and root words. However, it is not advisable to use them if your Teeline outlines are naturally large.

air, aer-......................, bronch-......................, cancer/carcino-......................, fibr-......................,

gastr-......................, investigate/ion......................, kidney......................, large......................,

uter-......................, vagin-......................

2 Prefixes/Suffixes and the Greek and Latin Equivalents of Medical Words

PREFIXES AND SUFFIXES

All medical words have their origins in either Latin or Greek and are made up of prefixes, roots and suffixes. A knowledge of these will allow the most complex medical term to be broken down into its component parts and so give the meaning, e.g.

dys	*men*	*orrhoea*
↓	↓	↓
difficult, painful, abnormal	month	excessive discharge, to flow

Therefore *dysmenorrhoea* means painful periods.

Where the Greek and Latin words for the same term are in common usage, these have been marked in the following list of prefixes and suffixes to avoid confusion.

The list is not comprehensive, but contains those words in frequent use. The very commonly used prefixes and suffixes (HYPER-, HYPO-, -OTOMY, -OSIS, etc.) will be learned quickly and so this section may be used purely for reference. However, examples are given for each prefix and suffix so that you can, if you wish, practise your own outlines. In most cases the meanings of each example can be worked out using the method described above.

Prefix/ suffix   **Meaning**   **Examples to practise**

Note: j = join; d = disjoin; G = Greek; L = Latin
The Teeline example given under each prefix/suffix refers to the first word of the 'Examples to practise' column.

A-/AN-   absence, without   *afebrile (without fever)*, amenorrhoea, anaemia, anaesthesia, anorexia, anosmia, apnoea, apyrexia, aseptic

e.g.

AB-   away from   *abductor (a muscle which draws a limb away from the midline of the body – opposite of adduct)*, abducent, ablation, abnormal

e.g.

ABDOMIN-   abdominal   *abdominoperineal (pertaining to the abdomen and perineum)*, abdominalgia, abdominocardiac, abdominopelvic

e.g.

Prefix/ suffix	**Meaning**	**Examples to practise**
ACR- .... e.g.	extremity	*acral (relating to ears, fingers, toes)*, acro-arthritis, acrocephaly, acrocyanosis, acrodynia, acromegaly, acromicria, acromion, acronyx, acroparaesthesia, acrophobia
ACTIN- .... e.g.	light, sunray	*actinism (action of spectral rays)*, actinobiology, actinodermatitis, actinomycin
AD- .... e.g.	towards	*adduct (to draw towards mid-line of body)*, adhesion, adnexa, adoral, adrenal, adsorbents, adsorption
ADEN- .... e.g.	glandular	*adenectomy* (removal of gland)*, adenitis, adenoid, adenoma, adenomyoma, adenopathy, adenosclerosis, adenovirus
		* See suffix -ECTOMY on page 29.
ADIPO- .... e.g.	fat	*adiposity (excessive fat in the body)*, adiposis, adipocele, adiposuria
AER- .... j *or* d e.g.	air	*aerobe (micro-organism which requires O_2)*, aerogenous, aerogram, aerophagia, aerosol
ALKA- .... e.g.	alkaline	*alkalaemia (excess of alkali)*, alkali, alkaline, alkalinuria, alkaloid, alkalosis
AMBI- .... e.g.	both	*ambidextrous (able to use both hands equally well)*, ambient, ambiopia, ambiparous, ambivalence
AMNIO- .... e.g.	foetal membrane	*amniocentesis (drawing fluid from foetal sac)*, amniography, amnion, amnioscopy, amniotic, amniotomy
AMYL- .... e.g.	starch	*amylase (enzyme which converts starch into sugars)*, amylnitrite, amylobarbitone, amylocaine, amyloid, amylolysis, amylopsin
ANDR- .... e.g.	male	*andria (pseudo-male hermaphrodite)*, androgens, androgyna, androphobia

Prefix/ suffix	Meaning	Examples to practise
ANGI-	vessel	*angiectasis (abnormal dilation of blood vessels)*, angiitis, angiocardiogram, angiogram, angioma, angioplasty, angiospasm
e.g.		
ANISO-	unequal	*anisocoria (inequality in diameter of pupils)*, anisocytosis, anisomelia, anisometropia
e.g.		
ANTE- ....d	before (time, place)	*anteflexion (bending forward)*, antemortem, antenatal, antepartum, anteverted
e.g.		
ANTI- ....d	against	*antibiotic (destroys organisms)*, antibody, anticholinergic, anticoagulant, anticonvulsant, antidote, anti-emetic, antihistamine, antimigraine, antiseptic, antitoxin, antiviral
e.g.		
AORT-	large artery	*aortitis (inflammation of aorta)*, aortic, aortogram, aortography
e.g.		
ARTHR-	joint	*arthralgia (pain in joint)*, arthrectomy, arthritis, arthroclasia, arthrodesis, arthrodynia, arthrogram, arthrography, arthropathy, arthroplasty, arthroscope, arthrosis, arthrotomy
e.g.		
AUD-	hearing	*auditory (pertaining to hearing)*, audiogram, audiology, audiometer
e.g.		
AUR-	ear	*aural (pertaining to ear)*, aural, auricle, auriscope
e.g.		
AUTO-	self	*autogenous (self-generated)*, autodiagnosis, autogenic, autohypnosis, autology, autolysis, autonomic, autophobia, autoplasty, auto-intoxication, autosuggestion, autotransfusion
j or d e.g.		
-AC	relating to	*cardiac (relating to the heart)*, amnesiac, haemophiliac, iliac
e.g.		
-AEMIA	blood	*alkalaemia (increased alkali in blood)*, acetonaemia, anaemia, anoxaemia, bacteraemia, cholaemia, glycaemia, hyperaemia, oligaemia, sapraemia, septicaemia, toxaemia, uraemia
e.g.		

Prefix/ suffix	Meaning	Examples to practise
-ALGIA .... e.g.	pain	*arthralgia (pain in joint)*, cardialgia, cephalalgia, cystalgia, dentalgia, gastralgia, hyperalgia, hysteralgia, metatarsalgia, myalgia, neuralgia, odontalgia, otalgia
-ASE .... e.g.	catalyst	*amylase (any enzyme which converts starches into sugars)*, kinase, lipase, peptidase
BACTER- .... G e.g.	rod	*bacteraemia (bacteria in blood)*, bacteria, bactericide, bacteriologist, bacteriolysis, bacteriostasis
BI- .... e.g.	two	*biceps (muscle with two points of origin)*, biconcave, biconvex, bicornuate, bicuspid, bifid, bifurcation, bilateral, bilobular, bimanual, binaural, binocular, binovular, biparietal, biparous
BILI- .... e.g.	bile	*biliary (pertaining to bile)*, bilious, bilirubin, biliuria, biliverdin
BRACHY- .... e.g.	short	*brachycephalic (short-headed)*, brachydactyly, brachyfacial, brachysicelic
BRONCH- .... e.g.	bronchi	*bronchiectasis (dilatation of bronchial tubes)*, bronchiole, bronchiolitis, bronchitis, broncho-adenitis, bronchodilator, bronchogenic, bronchogram, bronchography, bronchomycosis, bronchophony, bronchopneumonia, bronchoscope, bronchospasm, bronchospirometer, bronchotracheal
-BLAST .... e.g.	cell	*chondroblast (cell producing cartilage)*, erythroblast, fibroblast, lymphoblast, microblast, myeoblast, neuroblast, osteoblast, trophoblast
CAEC- .... e.g.	blind end	*caecum (commencement of colon)*, caecorectostomy, caecosigmoidostomy caecostomy
CALC- .... e.g.	chalk, line	*calcium (a constituent of bones and teeth)*, calcareous, calcification, calcified, calculus
CARB- .... e.g.	carbon	*carbamazepine (drug used in epilepsy)*, carbasone, carbenoxolone, carbohydrate, carboluria

Prefix/ suffix	Meaning	Examples to practise
CARCINO-	cancerous	*carcinogen (produces cancer)*, carcinogenesis, carcinogenic, carcinoma, carcinomatosis
CARDI-	heart	*cardiac (relating to heart)*, cardialgia, cardiodynia, cardiogenic, cardiogram, cardiology, cardiomegaly, cardiopathy, cardiophone, cardioplasty, cardiorraphy, cardioscope, cardiospasm, cardiothoracic, cardiovascular, cardioversion, carditis
CARP-	wrist	*carpal tunnel syndrome (numbness and tingling in hand)*, carpometacarpal, carpopedal, carpus
CAV-	hollow, cavern	*cavity (a hollow)*, cavamesenteric, cavernous, cavitation
CENTR-	centre	*centrifugal (tendency to move outwards)*, centrifuge, centripetal, centrosome
CEPHAL-	head	*cephalgia (headache)*, cephalhaematoma, cephalocele, cephalometry
CEREBR-	brain	*cerebral (pertaining to cerebrum)*, cerebration, cerebrospinal, cerebrovascular, cerebrum
CERVI-	neck	*cervical (pertaining to neck)*, cervicectomy, cervicitis, cervix
CHEMO-	chemical	*chemoprophylaxis (administration of chemicals to prevent disease)*, chemosuppressive, chemotaxis, chemotherapy

Prefix/ suffix	Meaning	Examples to practise
CHIR-	hand, manipu-lation	*chiropractic (manual movement of vertebrae)*, chiroplasty, chiropody, chiropractor, chiropraxis
e.g.		
CHLOR-	pale green	*chlorambucil (drug used in leukaemia)*, chlorbutol, chlordiazepoxide, chlorhexidine, chlorine, chloroform, chloroma
e.g.		
CHOL-	gall/bile	*cholaemia (bile in blood)*, cholagogue, cholangiogram, cholangiography, cholangitis
e.g.		
CHOLE-CYST-	gall-bladder	*cholecystangiogram (X-ray of gall-bladder)*, cholecystectomy, cholecystenterostomy, cholecystitis, cholecystogram, cholecystojejunostomy, cholecystostomy
e.g.		
CHOLE-DOCH-	bile duct	*choledochoduodenal (pertaining to bile ducts and duodenum)*, choledocholithiasis, choledochostomy, choledochotomy
e.g.		
CHONDR-	cartilage	*chondritis (inflammation of cartilage)*, chondroblast, chondrocostal, chondrocyte, chondrodynia, chondrolysis, chondroma, chondromalacia, chondrosarcoma
e.g.		
CHOR-	outer membrane	*chorion (outer membrane of embryonic sac)*, chorionepithelioma, chorioretinitis, choroid, choroiditis
e.g.		
CIRCUM-	around	*circumcision (to cut around, excision of foreskin)*, circumcorneal, cirumflex, circumoral, circumvallate
e.g.		
COL-	colon	*colectomy (excision of colon)*, colic, coliform, colitis colocystoplasty, colostomy, colotomy
e.g.		
COLP- ...G	vagina (L)	*colpitis (inflammation of vagina)*, colpocentesis, colpoperinorrhaphy, colpophotography, colporrhaphy, colposcope, colpotomy
e.g.		

Prefix/ suffix	Meaning	Examples to practise
COM-/CON-	together	*compression (the act of squeezing or pressing together)*, compatibility, compound, condense, confluent
e.g.		
CORT-	external layer	*cortex (outer layer of organ)*, corticoid, corticosteroids, cortisol, cortisone
e.g.		
CRANI-	skull	*craniectomy (removal of part of skull)*, craniofacial, craniometry, cranioplasty, craniosacral, craniotabes, craniotomy
e.g.		
CRYO-	cold	*cryogenic (produced by low temperature)*, cryopexy, cryoprobe, cryosurgery
e.g.		
CRYPT-	hidden	*cryptococcus (a genus of fungi)*, cryptogenic, cryptomenorrhoea, cryptorchism
e.g.		
CYCL-	circle	*cyclical (pertaining to a regular series of events)*, cyclitis, cyclodialysis, cyclodiathermy, cycloplegia, cyclothymia
e.g.		
CYST-	bladder	*cystalgia (pain in bladder)*, cystectomy, cystic, cystinosis, cystitis, cystocele, cystogram, cystolithiasis, cystometry, cystoplasty, cystoscope, cystostomy, cystotomy
e.g.		
CYTO-	cell	*cytodiagnosis (diagnosis by study of cells)*, cytology, cytolysis, cytopathic, cytoplasm, cytostasis, cytotoxic
e.g.		
-CELE	swelling	*cephalocele (hernia of brain)*, cystocele, encephalocele, enterocele, galactocele, haematocele, hydrocele, mucocele, myelocele, omphalocele, urethrocele
e.g.		
-CENTESIS d or j	puncturing	*amniocentesis (withdrawing of fluid from foetal sac)*, colpocentesis, paracentesis, pericardiocentesis, thoracentesis
e.g.		
-CIDE	destructive	*bactericide (agent which destroys bacteria)*, genocide, homocide, suicide
e.g.		

Prefix/ suffix	Meaning	Examples to practise
-COCCI/ -COCCUS	bacteria/ bacterium	*diplococci (bacteria occurring in pairs)*, cryptococcus, enterococcus, gonococci, meningococcus, micrococci, pneumococcus, staphylococci, streptococcus
-CYTE	cell	*fibrocyte (cell which gives rise to connective tissue)*, granulocyte, haematocyte, histiocyte, leucocyte, lymphocyte, macrocyte, monocyte, neurocyte, osteocyte, reticulocyte, thrombocyte
-CYTOSIS	increase in cells	*anisocytosis (inequality in size of cells)*, erythrocytosis leptocytosis, leucocytosis
DACRYO-	tear-drop	*dacryoadenitis (inflammation of tear gland)*, dacryocyst, dacryocystitis, dacryolith
DE-	away from	*decalcification (removal of mineral salts)*, decapsulation, decerebrate, decompensation, decompression, decongestion, defaecation, defibrillation, defibrinated, dehydration, deodorant, deoxygenation, depilate, desensitisation, detoxication
DENT-	tooth	*dentalgia (toothache)*, dental, dentifrice, dentine, dentistry, dentition, dentoid, denture
DERM-	skin	*dermatitis (inflammation of skin)*, dermatoglyphics, dermatology, dermatome, dermatomycosis, dermatophyte, dermatosis, dermis, dermographic
DI-/DIPLO-	two	*dicephalous (two-headed)*, dicrotic, diplegia, diplopia
DIA-	through	*diapedesis (passage of blood through vessel walls)*, diagnosis, diaphoresis, diaplacental, diathermy

Prefix/ suffix	**Meaning**	**Examples to practise**
DIS- .... e.g.	away from	*disarticulation (amputation at a joint)*, disinfectants, disinfestation, dislocation, disorientation
DORS- .... e.g.	back	*dorsal (pertaining to back)*, dorsiflexion, dorsocentral, dorsolumbar
DYS- .... e.g.	difficult, painful	*dysaesthesia (impairment of touch sensation)*, dyscrasia, dysentery, dysfunction, dyskinesia, dyslalia, dyslexia, dysmenorrhoea, dysopia, dyspareunia, dyspepsia, dysphagia, dysphasia, dysplasia, dyspnoea, dysrhythmia, dystaxia, dystocia, dystrophy, dysuria
-DERM/ -DERMA/ -DERMIA/ -DERMIS e.g.	skin	*ectoderm (external germ layer of embryo)*, endoderm, epidermis, erythrodermia, introderma, pachydermia, pyodermia, scleroderma, xeroderma
-DYNIA .... e.g.	pain	*acrodynia (painful extremities)*, arthrodynia, cardiodynia, chondrodynia, gastrodynia, mastodynia, pleurodynia
E- ..\.............. e.g.	lacking	*edentulous (lacking teeth)*, edentate, evacuate, eviscerate, evulsion
ECHO- .... e.g.	repetition	*echolalia (repetition of words heard)*, echo-encephalography, echophony, echopraxia
ECTO- .... e.g.	outside	*ectoderm (external layer of embryo)*, ectodermosis, ectoparasite, ectopic, ectozoa
ELECTR- ... e.g.	electricity	*electrocardiogram (record of heart contractions, etc)*, electrocoagulation, electrode, electrodiagnosis, electrolysis, electrolytes, electromyograph, electroplexy, electropyrexia, electrosection, electrotherapy
EMBOL- ... e.g.	plug	*embolectomy (removal of embolus)*, embolic, embolism, embologenic

Prefix/suffix	Meaning	Examples to practise
EN- e.g.	in, into, within	*encapsulated (enclosed in a capsule)*, encephalon, enchondroma, encysted, endartitis
ENCEPHAL- e.g.	brain	*encephalitis (inflammation of brain)*, encephalocele, encephalogram, encephaloma, encephalomalacia, encephalopathy
END- e.g.	in, into, within	*endarteritis (inflammation of lining coat of artery)*, endaural, endinopathy, endocarditis, endocervical, endocrinology, endoderm, endogenous, endometriosis, endometrium, endophlebitis, endoscope
ENTER- e.g.	intestine	*enteralgia (pain in intestines)*, enteritis, enterocele, enteroclysis, enterococcus, enterocolitis, enterolith, enterolithiasis, enterostomy, enterotomy, enterozoa
EPI- e.g.	upon, over, beside	*epicardium (visceral layer of pericardium)*, epicondyle, epicranium, epicystitis, epidemic, epidermis, epididymectomy, epididymis, epidural, epigastrium, epiglottis, epimenorrhoea, epiphora, episclera, epispinal, epistaxis, epithelioma
ERYTH- e.g.	red	*erythema (reddening of the skin)*, erythraemia, erythroblast, erythrocyanosis, erythrocytes, erythrocythaemia, erythrocytopenia, erythrocytosis, erythroderma, erythropoiesis
EU- e.g.	well, normal	*eugenics (science concerning improving future generations)*, eupepsia, euphoria, euthanasia, eutocia
EXTR- e.g.	outside	*extra-articular (outside a joint)*, extracapsular, extracardiac, extracellular, extracorporeal, extradural, extragenital, extrarenal, extra-uterine, extravenous, extrovert
-ECTOMY e.g.	removal of	*adenoidectomy (removal of adenoids)*, appendicectomy, cholecystectomy, cystectomy, embolectomy, gastrectomy, gingivectomy, hypophysectomy, hysterectomy, iridectomy, laminectomy, mastectomy, prostatectomy, sympathectomy, thyroidectomy, tonsillectomy
FIBR- e.g.	fibrous tissue	*fibrocartilage (cartilage containing fibrous tissue)*, fibrin, fibrochondritis, fibrocyst, fibroid, fibroma, fibromuscular, fibromyoma, fibrositis, fibrovascular

Prefix/ suffix	Meaning	Examples to practise
-FORM ⌐.... e.g. ⌐	having the form of	*coliform (bacterium)*, epileptiform, hydatidiform
GALACT- ...⌐......... G e.g. ⌐........	milk	*galactagogue (agent increasing milk)*, galactin, galactocele, galactorrhoea, galactosaemia, galactose
GASTR- ...⌐......... e.g. ⌐........	stomach	*gastralgia (stomach pain)*, gastrectasia, gastrectomy, gastritis, gastrocolic, gastroduodenal, gastro-enteritis, gastro-enterostomy, gastrogavage, gastrolavage, gastromalacia, gastroscopy, gastrostomy, gastrotomy
GEN- ...⌐... e.g. ...⌐....	generating	*genitalia (organs of generation)*, genes, genitocrural, genito-urinary
GLOSS- ⌐ ...⌐......... e.g. ⌐....	tongue	*glossectomy (excision of tongue)*, glossitis, glossopharyngeal, glossoplegia
GLUC- ...⌐... e.g. ⌐.......	sugar	*glucagon (hormone produced in pancreas)*, glucocorticoid, gluconeogenesis, glucose
GLYC- ...⌐... e.g. ⌐.......	sugar	*glycogen (animal starch)*, glycogenesis, glycolysis, glyconeogenesis, glycosuria, glycyrrhiza
GYNAECO- ...⌐............. e.g. ⌐.........	female	*gynaecology (science dealing with diseases peculiar to women)*, gynaecography, gynaecoid, gynaecomastia
-GENIC ...⌐.... e.g. ⌐.........	causative	*bronchogenic (arising from a bronchus)*, carcinogenic, cardiogenic, cryogenic, cryptogenic, dysmorphogenic, eugenic, iatrogenic, neurogenic, osteogenic, pyogenic

Prefix/ suffix	Meaning	Examples to practise
-GENOUS	formation, origin	*aerogenous (gas producing)*, endogenous, haematogenous, heterogenous, homogenous, myelogenous
e.g.		
-GOGUE	increasing flow	*cholagogue (drug which increases flow of bile)*, galactagogue, helminthagogue, sialagogue
e.g.		
-GRAM	tracing, picture	*aortogram (film showing aorta after injection of radiopaque medium)*, angiogram, arteriogram, arthrogram, bronchogram, cardiogram, cholangiogram, cholecystogram, chromatogram, pyelogram, renogram, salpingogram, tomogram
e.g.		
-GRAPH/Y	description, writing	*arthrography (X-ray of joint)*, aortograph, bronchography, cardiograph, discograph, encephalography, gastrography, mammography, myelography, salpingography, venography
e.g.		
HAEM-	blood	*haemangioma (malformation of blood vessel)*, haemarthrosis, haematemesis, haematocele, haematology, haematoma, haematozoon, haematuria, haemodialysis, haemoglobin, haemolytic, haemophiliac, haemoptysis, haemorrhage, haemorrhoids, haemostasis
e.g.		
HEMI- d or j	half	*hemianaesthesia (loss of touch/sense down one side of body)*, hemianopia, hemiatrophy, hemichorea, hemicolectomy, hemicrania, hemidiaphoresis, hemifacial, hemiglossectomy, hemiparesis, hemiplegia
e.g.		
HEPA-	liver	*heparin (acid present in liver)*, hepatalgia, hepatectomy, hepatic, hepatico-enteric, hepatitis, hepatization, hepatocellular hepatocirrhosis, hepatoma, hepatomegaly, hepatotoxic
e.g.		
HETERO-	other, different	*heterogenous (of unlike origin)*, heterologous, heteroplasty, heterosexual
e.g.		
HEX-	six	*hexamine (urinary antiseptic)*, hexachlorophene, hexobarbitone, hexoestrol, hexose
e.g.		

Prefix/ suffix	Meaning	Examples to practise
HOMO- ⌐... e.g.	same	*homogenous (same nature)*, homograft, homolateral, homologous, homonymous, homoplasty, homosexual, homotransplant, homozygous
HYDR- ... . e.g.	water	*hydraemia (excess plasma in blood)*, hydrarthrosis, hydroa, hydrocele, hydrocephalic, hydrolysis, hydrometer, hydronephrosis, hydropathy, hydrophobia, hydrotherapeutics, hydrothorax
HYPER- ...d e.g.	over, excessive	*hyperacidity (excess of acid)*, hyperaemia, hyperaesthesia, hyperalgia, hyperasthenia, hyperemesis, hyperglycaemic, hyperkeratosis, hypermetropia, hypermobility, hypernutrition, hyperphagia, hyperplasia, hypersensitive, hypertension, hyperthermia, hyperthyroidism, hypertrophy
HYPO- ....d e.g.	under, deficiency	*hypo-aesthesia (diminished sensitivity)*, hypocalcaemia, hypodermic, hypofunction, hypoglossal, hypoglycaemic, hypomania, hypopiesis, hypoplasia, hypotension, hypothalamus, hypothermia, hypothyroidism, hypotonia, hypoventilation, hypoxia
HYSTER- e.g.	uterus	*hysterectomy (removal of uterus)*, hysteria, hysteritis, hysterocarcinoma, hysterocervicotomy, hysterology, hysteromyoma, hysteropathy, hysteroptosis, hysterospasm, hysterotomy
ILE- ... e.g.	bowel, ileum	*ileectomy (removal of ileum)*, ileitis, ileocolic, ileocolitis, ileocolostomy, ileocystoplasty, ileoproctostomy, ileorectal, ileostomy
ILIO- ... e.g.	bone, ilium	*iliococcygeal (pertaining to ilium and coccyx)*, iliofemoral, iliopectineal, iliopsoas
IM-/IN- e.g.	not, into, within	*incision (cutting into body tissue using a sharp knife)*, implant, imperforate, infertility
IMMUN- e.g.	immunity	*immunization (process of increasing specific antibody in tissues)*, immunogenesis, immunoglobulins, immunology, immunopathology, immunosensitivity, immunosuppressive, immunotherapy, immunotransfusion

Prefix/ suffix	Meaning	Examples to practise
INFRA-	below	*infraclavicular (below the clavicle)*, infra-orbital, infra-red rays, infraspinous
e.g.		
INTER-	between	*interarticular (between joints)*, interatrial, intercellular, interclavicular, intercondyle, intercostal, intercourse, interlobar, intermenstrual, interphalangeal, interspinous, interstitial, interventricular, intervertebral
e.g.		
INTRA-	within	*intracellular (within a cell)*, intracerebral, intracranial, intradermal, intragastric, intrahepatic, intramuscular, intranasal, intra-ocular, intraperitoneal, intrapharyngeal, intraspinal, intratracheal, intra-uterine, intravenous
.... j *or* d		
e.g.		
IRID-	iris, rainbow	*iridectomy (excision of part of iris)*, iridencleisis, iridocele, iridocyclitis, iridodialysis, iridotomy
e.g.		
ISO-	equal	*isotonic (equal tension)*, iso-immunization, isometric, isotopes
e.g.		
-ITIS	inflam- mation	*adenitis (inflammation of gland)*, angitis, appendicitis, arthritis, blepharitis, bronchitis, colitis, dermatitis, diverticulitis, endometritis, enteritis, gastritis, gingivitis, osteomyelitis, otitis, pancreatitis, peritonitis, pharyngitis, phlebitis
.... j *or* d		
e.g.		
KERAT-	horn, skin, cornea,	*keratectomy (removal of portion of cornea)*, keratin, keratitis, keratoconus, kerato-iritis, keratolysis, keratoma, keratometer, keratopathy, keratoplasty, keratoscope, keratosis, keratotomy
e.g.		
KIN-	motion	*kinematics (science of motion)*, kinaesthesis, kineplastic, kinetic
e.g.		
LACT- L	milk	*lactation (secretion of milk)*, lactagogue, lactalbumin, lactase, lacteals, lactiferous, lactifuge, lactogenic, lactosuria
e.g.		
LARYNG-	larynx	*laryngectomy (removal of larynx)*, laryngitis, laryngofissure, laryngologist, laryngoparalysis, laryngopharynx, laryngoscope, laryngospasm, laryngostenosis, laryngostomy, laryngotomy
e.g.		

Prefix/ suffix	Meaning	Examples to practise
LEPTO- ⌇... e.g. ⌇........	thin, soft	*leptocytosis (thin red-blood cells)*, leptomeningitis, leptospirosis, leptothrix
LEUC-/ LEUK- ⌇...... e.g. ⌇........	white	*leucocyte (white corpuscles in blood)*, leucocytosis, leucoderma, leucoma, leuconychia, leucopenia, leucopoiesis, leucorrhoea, leucotomy, leukaemia, leukoplakia
LIP- ⌇......... e.g. ⌇..........	fat	*lipaemia (increased fat in blood)*, lipase, lipoid, lipoidosis, lipolysis, lipoma, lipuria
LITH- ⌇.... e.g. ⌇........	stone	*lithiasis (formation of calculi)*, litholapaxy, lithotrite, lithuresis
LYMPH- ⌇. e.g. ⌇......	part of blood plasma	*lymphadenectomy (removal of lymph node)*, lymphadenoma, lymphadenopathy, lymphangitis, lymphatic, lymphocyte, lymphocytosis, lymphoedema, lymphoid, lymphoma, lymphorrhagia, lymphosarcoma
-LITH ⌇.. e.g. ⌇..........	stone	*dacrolith (stone in tear duct)*, cystolithy, phlebolith, sialolith, tonsillolith
-LITHI- ASIS ⌇.... e.g. ⌇......	presence of stones	*cholecystolithiasis (stones in gall-bladder)*, choledocholithiasis, cystolithiasis, enterolithiasis, nephrolithiasis, urolithiasis
-LYSIS/ -LYTIC ⌇ ⌇........ e.g. ⌇.......	breaking down	*amylolysis (digestion of starch)*, autolysis, catalytic chondrolysis, cytolysis, electrolysis, fibrinolytic, glycolysis, histolysis, hydrolysis, mucinolysis, onycholytic, pneumolysis
MACRO- ⌇.......... e.g. ⌇.......	large	*macrocephalous (excessive development of head)*, macrocheilia, macrocyte, macrocythaemia, macrodactyly, macroglossia, macrolymphocyte, macromastia, macrophages, macroscopic

Prefix/ suffix	Meaning	Examples to practise
MAL-	abnormal, bad	*malabsorption (poor absorption)*, maladjustment, malalignment, malaria, malassimilation, malformation, malnutrition, malocclusion, malposition, malpractice, malpresentation
e.g.		
MAST- ......G	breast	*mastalgia (pain in breast)*, mastectomy, mastitis, mastography, mastoid, mastoidectomy, mastoidotomy
e.g.		
MEDI-	middle	*media (middle coat of vessel)*, medial, median, mediastinum, mediolateral
e.g.		
MEDIC-	remedy, to heal	*medicochirurgical (pertaining to both medicine and surgery)*, medicament, medicinal, medicosocial
e.g.		
MEGA-	large	*megacolon (dilated and elongated colon)*, megakaryocyte, megaloblast, megalocephalic, megalomania
e.g.		
MELAN-	black, pigment	*melaena (black stools)*, melanin, melanoma, melanosarcoma, melanosis, melanuria
e.g.		
MEN-	month	*menopause (stopping of menstruation)*, menorrhagia, menses, menstrual
e.g.		
MENING-	membrane (of brain)	*meningioma (a slow-growing, usually benign, tumour)*, meningitis, meningocele, meningococcus, meningo-encephalitis
e.g.		
MES-	middle	*mesarteritis (inflammation of middle coat of artery)*, mesencephalon, mesentery, mesoderm
e.g.		
META-	between, change	*metabolic (pertaining to metabolism)*, metacarpophalangeal, metacarpus, metaphysis, metaplasia, metatarsalgia, metatarsus
e.g.		

Prefix/ suffix	Meaning	Examples to practise
METHYL-	methane	*methylamphetamine (stimulant)*, methylated, methyldopa, methylene, methylprednisolone
MICRO-	small	*microbiology (study of micro-organisms)*, microblast, microcardia, microcephalic, micrococcus, microcyte, microdontic, micrognathia, micrometer, micro-organisms, microphage, microscopic, microtome
MON-	single	*monarticular (relating to one joint)*, monocular, monocyte, monomania, mononuclear, mononucleosis, monoplegia
MUC- L	mucus	*mucin (glycoproteins found in cells)*, mucinase, mucinolysis, mucocele
MULTI- d	many	*multicellular (many cells)*, multigravida, multilobular, multilocular, multinuclear, multipara
MY-	muscle	*myasthenia (muscular weakness)*, myatonia, myocardium, myocele, myoclonus, myoelectric, myofibrosis, myogenic, myokymia, myoma, myomectomy, myoneural, myopathy, myoplasty
MYC-	fungal	*mycelium (mass of fungi)*, mycetoma, mycology, mycosis
MYEL-	spinal cord, bone marrow	*myelin (white substance in a nerve)*, myelitis, myelocele, myelocytes, myelofibrosis, myelogenous, myelogram, myeloid, myeloma, myelomeningocele, myelopathy
MYRING-	eardrum	*myringitis (inflammation of eardrum)*, myringoplasty, myringotome, myringotomy
MYXO- G	mucus	*myxoedema (hypothyroidism)*, myxoma, myxosarcoma, myxovirus

Prefix/ suffix	Meaning	Examples to practise
-MALACIA	softening	*chondromalacia (softening of cartilage)*, encephalomalacia, gastromalacia, keratomalacia, myomalacia, osteomalacia
-MEGALY	large	*acromegaly (large extremities)*, cardiomegaly, hepatomegaly, splenomegaly
-METER	measure	*cephalometer (instrument for measuring the head)*, craniometer, cystometer, hydrometer, hygrometer, micrometer, ophthalmotonometer, optometer, thermometer, urethrometer
NARCO-	stupor	*narco-analysis (analysis of mentality under light anaesthesia)*, narcolepsy, narcosis, narcosynthesis, narcotherapy
NAS-	nose	*nasogastric (pertaining to nose and stomach)*, nasal, nasolacrimal, naso-oesophageal, nasopharyngoscope, nasopharyngitis, nasopharynx
NEO-	new	*neo-arthrosis (abnormal articulation)*, neologism, neonate, neonatorum, neoplasia
NEPHR-	kidney	*nephralgia (pain in kidney)*, nephrectomy, nephritis, nephrocalcinosis, nephrocapsulectomy, nephrogenic, nephrogram, nephrolithiasis, nephrology, nephroplasty, nephrosis
NEUR-	nerve	*neuralgia (pain in nerve)*, neurectomy, neuritis, neuroblast, neurocyte, neurodermatitis, neurofibroma, neurologist, neuromuscular, neuropathy, neuroplasty, neurosis, neurosurgery, neurotic, neurotomy, neurotoxic
NOCT-	night	*noctambulation (sleep-walking)*, noctalgia, nocturia, nocturnal

Prefix/ suffix	Meaning	Examples to practise
NORMO-	normal	*normoblast (normal-sized red-blood cell)*, normocyte, normoglycaemic, normotension, normothermia, normotonic
e.g.		
NUCLE-	kernel	*nucleated (possessing one or more nuclei)*, nucleoproteins, nucleotoxic, nucleus
e.g.		
NYCT- ......G	night	*nyctalgia (pain at night)*, nyctalopia, nyctophobia, nycturia
e.g.		
-NATAL	birth	*neonatal (newly born)*, antenatal, perinatal, postnatal
e.g.		
OCUL-	eye	*ocular (pertaining to the eye)*, oculentum, oculist, oculogenital, oculogyric, oculomotor
e.g.		
ODONT-	tooth	*odontalgia (toothache)*, odontitis, odontoid, odontolith, odontology, odontoma, odontoprisis, odontotherapy, odontotomy
e.g.		
OESO-PHAG-	gullet	*oesophagectasis (dilated gullet)*, oesophagitis, oesophagectomy, oesophagoscope, oesophagostomy
e.g.		
OLIG-	deficient	*oligaemia (lack of blood)*, oligohydramnios, oligomenorrhoea, oligophrenia, oligospermia, oliguria
e.g.		
OMPHAL-	navel	*omphalitis (inflammation of the umbilicus)*, omphalocele, omphaloproptosis, omphalus
e.g.		
ONYCH-	nail	*onychia (inflammation of the nail)*, onychocryptosis, onychogryphosis, onycholysis, onychomycosis
e.g.		

Prefix/ suffix	Meaning	Examples to practise
OO- ...⌇....G e.g.	ovum	*oocyte (immature ovum)*, oogenesis, oophorectomy, oophoritis, oophoron, oophorosalpingectomy, oosperm
OPHTH- ALM- ....↗... e.g. ...↗.......	eye	*ophthalmia (inflammation of eye)*, ophthalmic, ophthalmitis, ophthalmologist, ophthalmoplegia, ophthalmoscope, ophthalmotonometer
ORCHI- .ℓ... e.g. .ℓ⌐........	testis	*orchidectomy (castration)*, orchidopexy, orchiepididymitis, orchis, orchitis
ORTHO- ...⌐.. e.g.	straight	*orthodontic (pertaining to the straightening of the teeth)*, orthopaedic, orthoptics, orthostatic
OS-/OSS- ...↙. e.g.	bone, mouth	*ossification (the conversion of cartilage into bone)*, cervical os, os calcis, osseous, ossicle, osteitis
OSTE- ....G e.g.	bone	*osteitis (inflammation of bone)*, osteo-arthritis, osteoblast, osteochondritis, osteoclasis, osteocyte, osteodystrophy, osteolytic, osteomalacia, osteomyelitis, osteopath, osteophony, osteoplasty, osteoporosis, osteosarcoma, osteotomy
OT- .... e.g.	ear	*otalgia (earache)*, otitis, otolaryngology, otoliths, otologist, otomycosis, otorhinolaryngology, otorrhoea, otosclerosis, otoscope, ototoxic
OVARI- ...√.. L e.g. ...√.........	egg	*ovarian (pertaining to ovary)*, ovariectomy, ovariotomy, ovaritis
-OID ...↩... e.g.	resem- blance	*rheumatoid (resembling rheumatism)*, adenoid, dentoid, dermoid, endothelioid, lichenoid, lipoid, lymphoid, mastoid, myeloid, sarcoid, sphenoid
-(O)LOGY/ -(O)LOGICAL/ -(O)LOGIST .... d e.g. ...6........	study of	*biologist (scientist studying living things)*, cardiologist, cytology, endocrinologist, gynaecologist, histology, immunological, physiological, psychology, rhinologist

Prefix/ suffix	Meaning	Examples to practise
-OMA tumour	tumour	*adenoma (tumour of glandular tissue)*, angioma, atheroma, carcinoma, chondroma, cystadenoma, encephaloma, fibroma, glaucoma, haematoma, hepatoma, lipoma, lymphoma, meningioma, myeloma, myoma, myxoma, papilloma, sarcoma
e.g.		
-OPIA	eye	*myopia (short-sightedness)*, nyctalopia, polyopia, presbyopia
e.g.		
-(O)RRH-AGIA	flow	*blennorrhagia (mucous discharge)*, menorrhagia, metrorrhagia, otorrhagia, proctorrhagia, ulorrhagia
e.g.		
-(O)RRH-APHY	suturing	*achillorrhaphy (stitching Achilles tendon)*, arteriorrhaphy, blepharorrhaphy, cardiorrhaphy, colporrhaphy, herniorrhaphy, neurorrhaphy, perineorrhaphy
e.g.		
-(O)RRH-OEA	excessive discharge	*amenorrhoea (absence of periods)*, blennorrhoea, bronchorrhoea, cryptomenorrhoea, diarrhoea, dysmenorrhoea, galactorrhoea, gonorrhoea, haematorrhoea, pyorrhoea, rhinorrhoea, seborrhoea, steatorrhoea, trichorrhoea
e.g.		
-(O)SCOPE/ -(O)SCOPY/ -(O)SCOPIC	instrument for exam- ining/visual examination	*auriscope (instrument for examining the ear)*, bronchoscopy, cytoscope, gastroscope, hysteroscopy, laryngoscope, macroscopic, microscopic, ophthalmoscope, otoscopy, pneumoscope, proctoscopy, retinoscope, rhinoscope, sigmoidoscopy, stethoscope, tracheoscopy
e.g.		
-OSIS d	disease, condition	*acidosis (condition where alkali reserve is depleted)*, anastomosis, angiosclerosis, arteriosclerosis, arthrosis, cheilosis, chromatosis, dermatosis, diverticulosis, dyshidrosis, halitosis, lordosis, narcosis, nephrosis, neurosis, psychosis, scoliosis, tuberculosis
e.g.		
-(O)STOMY	opening	*cholecystostomy (opening of drainage after gall-bladder operation)*, colostomy, cystostomy, enterostomy, gastrostomy, ileostomy, jejunostomy, nephrostomy, oesophagostomy, sigmoidostomy, thoracostomy
e.g.		

Prefix/ suffix	Meaning	Examples to practise
-(O)TOME	cutting instrument	*costatome (rib shears)*, cystitome, dermatome, keratome, microtome, myringotome, osteotome
e.g.		
-(O)TOMY	incision	*cardiotomy (incision into heart)*, colpotomy, craniotomy, cystotomy, duodenotomy, enterotomy, episiotomy, gastrotomy, herniotomy, laparotomy, lobotomy, myotomy, nephrotomy, pubiotomy, rectocystotomy, septotomy, tenotomy, tracheotomy, vagotomy
e.g.		
PACHY- ...d	thick	*pachyblepharon (thick eyelids)*, pachycephalia, pachychilia, pachydermia, pachymeningitis
e.g.		
PAN-	all	*panarthritis (inflammation of all joints)*, pancarditis, pandemic, panhysterectomy, panophthalmitis, panosteitis
e.g.		
PANCREA-	pancreas	*pancreatectomy (excision of part or all of pancreas)*, pancreatin, pancreatitis, pancreatrophic
e.g.		
PARA-/ PARO-	beside, beyond	*para-aortic (near aorta)*, parahepatitis, paramedian, paramedical, paranasal, paranoia, paraplegia, pararectal, parasagittal, parasympathetic, parathyroid, paratyphoid, paravaginal, paronychia, parosmia, parotid, parotitis
e.g.		
PATHO- ..d	disease	*pathogen (disease-producing agent)*, pathogenesis, pathognomic, pathology, pathophobia
e.g.		
PED- ...|...... L	foot	*pedascope (the use of fluoroscopy to check shoe fitting)*, pedicle, pediculosis, peduncle
e.g.		
PER- ...|...... L	through	*percolation (straining through)*, percutaneous, perforation, permeability, peroral, per rectal, perspiration, per vagina
e.g.		

Prefix/ *suffix*	*Meaning*	*Examples to practise*
PERI- ..../............G d e.g. ..../..√.....	around	*perianal (surrounding anus)*, peri-arthritis, pericardectomy, pericardium, pericolitis, pericorneal, pericranium, perigastric, perilymph, perinatal, peripheral, peritoneum
PHARYNG- ...../.7.............. e.g. ...../.9.⌐........	pharynx	*pharyngectomy (removal of part of pharynx)*, pharyngismus, pharyngitis, pharyngolaryngeal, pharyngoplasty, pharyngotomy
PHLEB- $\mathcal{6}$... e.g. $\mathcal{6}$⌐..........	vein	*phlebectomy (removal of vein)*, phlebitis, phlebogram, phlebography, phlebolith, phlebothrombosis, phlebotomy
PHOT- ⌐....... e.g. ⌐.⌐........	light	*photalgia (pain in eyes after exposure to intense light)*, photochemical, photocoagulation, photo-endoscopy, photophobia, photosensitive, phototherapy
PILO- ...√... L e.g. √........... .....√.............	hair	*pilomotor nerves (nerves attached to hair follicle)*, pilonidal, pilosebaceous, pilosis
PLASM- 6..... e.g. 6....⌐°...	blood fluid	*plasmapherisis (taking blood from a donor)*, plasmin, plasminogen, plasmodium
PLEUR- .6.... e.g. 6..⌐..	rib	*pleurisy (inflammation of pleura)*, pleurodesis, pleurodynia, pleuropulmonary
PNEUM- ?⌐⌐ e.g. ..?⌐ç........	lung	*pneumococci (bacteria causing pneumonia)*, pneumatocele, pneumaturia, pneumoconiosis, pneumogastric, pneumolysis, pneumomycosis, pneumonectomy, pneumonitis, pneumoperitoneum, pneumoradiography
POD- ..⌐......... e.g. ..⌐..√........	foot	*podagra (gout (in the big toe))*, podalic, podarthritis, podopompholyx

Prefix/suffix	Meaning	Examples to practise
POLY-	many	*polyarteritis (inflammation of many arteries)*, polyarthralgia, polyarthritis, polycystic, polycythaemia, polydactyl, polydipsia, polygraph, polyneuritis, polyopia, polypectomy, polypoid, polyposis, polyuria
POST-	after	*post-coital (after intercourse)*, postepileptic, posthepatic, posthumous, postmature, post-mortem, postnatal, postoperative, postpartum, postprandial, postvaccinal
PRE- L d	before	*pre-anaesthetic (before an anaesthetic)*, precancerous, prediabetes, pre-eclampsia, prefrontal, premedication, premenstrual, premolars, prenatal, pre-operative, preparalytic, presystole
PRO- G d	before	*prodromal (period before infection and first symptom)*, progestation, proglottis, prolactin, prostate, prostatectomy, prostatitis, prothrombin, provitamin
PROCT-	anus	*proctalgia (rectum pain)*, proctitis, proctoclysis, proctocolectomy, proctocolitis, proctoscope, proctosigmoiditis
PSEUDO- ...j or d	false	*pseudo-angina (false angina)*, pseudo-arthrosis, pseudocoxalgia, pseudocrisis, pseudocyesis, pseudomonas, pseudomucin, pseudoparalysis, pseudoplegia, pseudopodia, pseudopolyposis
PSYCH-	mind	*psychiatrist (one who treats mental disorders)*, psycho-analysis, psychogenic, psychology, psychomotor, psychoneurosis, psychopath, psychosis, psychosomatic, psychotherapy, psychotic, psychotropic
PY-	pus	*pyaemia (septicaemia)*, pyarthrosis, pyodermia, pyogenic, pyometra, pyonephrosis, pyopericarditis, pyopneumothorax, pyorrhoea, pyosalpinx, pyothorax, pyuria
PYEL-	kidney, pelvis	*pyelitis (inflammation of kidney)*, pyelography, pyelolithotomy, pyelonephritis, pyeloplasty, pyelostomy

Prefix/ suffix	Meaning	Examples to practise
PYLORO- ✓. e.g. ✓~✓	pylorus (gatekeeper to stomach)	*pyloroduodenal (pertaining to pyloric sphincter and duodenum)*, pyloromyotomy, pyloroplasty, pylorospasm
PYR- ..✓...... e.g. ...✗..	fever	*pyrexia (fever)*, pyrimethamine, pyrogen, pyromania, pyrosis, pyrotherapy
-PATH/ -PATHIC/ -PATHY ..╷╷╷......d e.g. ~╷	disease	*adenopathy (disease of a gland)*, arthropathy, cardiopathic, cytopathy, encephalopathy, endinopathy, myelopathy, nephropathy, osteoarthropathy, osteopath, retinopathy, psychopath, stomatopathy
-PENIA ..╷.... e.g. ...ᒉ....	lack of	*leucopenia (decreased number of leucocytes)*, erythropenia, lymphopenia, neutropenia, thrombocytopenia
-PEXY ......↙... e.g. ....ᡆ	fixing	*cryopexy (fixing of detached retina)*, cystopexy, cysto-urethropexy, gastropexy, nephropexy, orchidopexy
-PHAGE/ -PHAGIA ....ᕃ.....ᕃ... e.g. ....ᕃ..	eating, swallowing	*aerophagia (swallowing of air)*, dysphagia, hyperphagia, macrophage
-PHIL/ -PHILIA ....ℓ...ℓ....... e.g. ...ℓℓ.....	affinity for	*basophilia (increase of basophils in the blood)*, haemophilia, neutrophil, pyrophilia, thermophil
-PHOBIA ᕃ. e.g. ᕫᕃ...	fear	*acrophobia (fear of heights)*, agoraphobia, androphobia, autophobia, claustrophobia, hydrophobia, mysophobia, nyctophobia, pathophobia, photophobia

Prefix/suffix	Meaning	Examples to practise
-PHONY	voice, sound	*bronchophony (lung sounds)*, cardiophony, echophony, osteophony
-PLASIA	formation	*dysplasia (abnormal formation)*, aplasia, hyperplasia, hypoplasia
-PLASTY	recon-structive surgery	*angioplasty (plastic surgery of blood vessels)*, cheiloplasty, cardioplasty, cranioplasty, gastroplasty, hernioplasty, mammaplasty, myringoplasty, pyeloplasty, pyloroplasty, rhinoplasty
-PLEGIA	paralysis	*diplegia (symmetrical paralysis of legs)*, gastroplegia, glossoplegia, iridoplegia, monoplegia, ophthalmoplegia, paraplegia, phrenoplegia, pseudoplegia, quadriplegia, tetraplegia
-PNOEA	breathing	*apnoea (without respiration)*, dyspnoea, hyperpnoea, tachypnoea
-PTOSIS	falling	*blepharoptosis (closed eyelid)*, carpoptosis, gastroptosis, hysteroptosis, metroptosis, nephroptosis, onychocryptosis, proptosis, visceroptosis
RADIO- j *or* d	radiation	*radio-active (giving off penetrating rays)*, radiobiology, radiodermatitis, radiographer, radiologist, radiosensitive, radiotherapy
RE-	back, again	*recalcitrant (condition resistant to treatment)*, recannulation, regression, regurgitation, relaxant, remission, remittant, repression, revascularization
RETICULO-	net-like (small)	*reticulocyte (young blood cell)*, reticulocytoma, reticulocytosis, reticulo-endothelial, reticuloses

Prefix/ suffix	Meaning	Examples to practise
RETIN- e.g.	net-like (large)	*retinitis (inflammation of retina)*, retinoblastoma, retinopathy, retinoscope
RETRO- e.g.	behind	*retrobulbar (back of eyeball)*, retrocaecal, retroflexion, retrogression, retro-ocular, retroperitoneal, retropharyngeal, retroplacental, retropleural, retrospection, retrosternal
RHIN- e.g.	nose	*rhinitis (inflammation of nasal mucous membrane)*, rhinology, rhinophyma, rhinoplasty, rhinorrhoea, rhinosporidosis, rhinovirus
SACRO- e.g.	sacrum	*sacro-anterior (breech presentation)*, sacrococcygeal, sacro-iliac, sacrolumbar, sacroposterior
SALPING- e.g.	Fallopian tube	*salpingectomy (removal of Fallopian tube)*, salpingitis, salpingogram, salpingo-oophorectomy, salpingostomy
SARCO- e.g.	flesh	*sarcoid (lesions in skin)*, sarcoidosis, sarcolemma, sarcoma
SCLER- e.g.	hard	*sclera (white of eye)*, scleritis, sclerocorneal, scleroderma, scleroma, sclerosis, sclerotomy
SEMI- ...d e.g.	half	*semicomatose (bordering on unconscious)*, semilunar, semipermeable, semiprone
SERO- e.g.	serum	*serology (study of sera)*, seropurulent, serosa, serositis
SIN- e.g.	hollow, cavity	*sinogram (X-ray of sinus)*, sinus, sinusitis, sinusoid
SPERM- e.g.	seed	*spermatic (pertaining to conveyance of sperm)*, spermaticidal, spermatogenesis, spermatorrhoea, spermatozoon, spermicide

Prefix/ suffix	Meaning	Examples to practise
SPHYGM-	pulse	*sphygmocardiograph (instrument which records pulse and heart beats)*, sphygmic, sphygmograph, sphygmomanometer
e.g.		
SPIR-	spiral	*spirillum (corkscrew-shaped bacteria)*, spirochaetaemia, spirochaete, spirograph, spirometer, spironolactone
e.g.		
SPLEN-	spleen	*splenectomy (removal of spleen)*, splenitis, splenocaval, splenogram splenomegaly, splenoportal, splenorenal
e.g.		
STEATO-	fat	*steatosis (fatty degeneration)*, steatoma, steatopygia, steatorrhoea
e.g.		
STERN-	sternum	*sternoclavicular (pertaining to the sternum and clavicle)*, sternal, sternocostal, sternotomy, sternum
e.g.		
SUB-	below, under	*subacute (moderately severe)*, subarachnoid, subclavian, subconscious, subcortical, subcostal, subcutaneous, subdural, subglottic, subhepatic, sublingual, sublobular, submucosa, subnormal, subnasal, subphrenic, subscapular, substernal
e.g.		
SUPER-	over	*supercilium (eyebrow)*, superego, superior, supernatant, supernumerary
e.g.		
SUPRA-	on, over, above	*supraclavicular (above collar bone)*, supracondyle, supracostal, supracranial, supranasal, supra-orbital, suprapelvic, suprapubic, suprarenal, supraseptal, suprasternal, supratonsillar
e.g.		
SYM-/SYN-	joined together	*syndactyl (webbed fingers/toes)*, symblepharon, symphysis, syndrome, synechia, synergism, synergist
e.g.		
-STASIS	stopping movement	*haemostasis (arrest of bleeding)*, cytostasis, homeostasis, lymphostasis
e.g.		
TACH-	swift	*tachistoscope (used to train word-blind people)*, tachycardia, tachyplasia, tachypnoea
e.g.		

Prefix/ suffix	Meaning	Examples to practise
TARS-	foot, edge of eyelid	*tarsalgia (pain in foot)*, tarsometatarsal, tarsoplasty, tarsorrhaphy
e.g.		
TENO-	tendon	*tenoplasty (plastic operation on tendon)*, tenorrhaphy, tenosynovitis, tenotomy
e.g.		
TERATO-	monster	*teratogen (agent which will produce an abnormal foetus)*, teratogenesis, teratology, teratoma
e.g.		
TETRA-	four	*tetracoccus (bacteria)*, tetracycline, tetradactylous, tetraplegia
e.g.		
THERM-	heat	*thermal (pertaining to heat)*, thermatology, thermogenesis, thermography, thermolabile, thermolysis, thermometer, thermophil, thermoplegia, thermostable, thermotherapy
e.g.		
THORAC-	thorax	*thoracentesis (withdrawing of fluid from the thorax)*, thoracic, thoraco-abdominal, thoracolumbar, thoracoplasty, thoracoscope, thoracotomy
e.g.		
THROMB-	clot	*thrombectomy (removal of thrombus)*, thrombin, thrombitis, thrombo-angiitis, thrombo-arteritis, thrombocytes, thrombo-embolic, thromboid, thrombolytic, thrombophlebitis, thromboplastin, thrombosis
e.g.		
THYM-	soul, gland in chest	*thymectomy (excision of thymus)*, thymoma, thymosin, thymus
e.g.		
THYRO-	thyroid gland	*thyroglossal (relating to thyroid and tongue)*, thyroidectomy, thyroiditis, thyrotomy, thyrotoxicosis, thyrotrophic, thyroxine
....j or d		
e.g.		

Prefix/suffix	Meaning	Examples to practise
TONSIL- ...... e.g.	tonsil	*tonsillectomy (removal of tonsils)*, tonsillitis, tonsilloliths, tonsillotome
TOX- .... e.g.	poison	*toxaemia (poisoning of body)*, toxicity, toxicology, toxicomania, toxin, toxoid, toxoplasmosis
TRACHE- .... e.g.	trachea	*tracheitis (inflammation of trachea)*, trachelorrhaphy, tracheobronchial, tracheo-oesophageal, tracheostomy, tracheotomy
TRANS- .... j *or* d e.g.	across, through	*transabdominal (through abdomen)*, transamniotic, transection, transfrontal, transfusion, translocation, translucent, transnasal, transplacental, transplant, transrectal, transurethral, transvaginal, transvesical
TRI- .... e.g.	three	*triceps (three-headed muscle in arm)*, tricuspid, trigeminal, trigone, trisomy
TRICH- .... e.g.	hair	*trichiasis (eyelashes causing friction on eyeball)*, trichinosis, trichophyton, trichuriasis
TUBER- .... e.g.	small lump	*tubercle (small prominence on bone)*, tuberculide, tuberculin, tuberculoid, tuberculoma, tuberculosis, tuberculostatic, tuberosity
TYMPAN- .... e.g.	drum	*tympanic (pertaining to eardrum)*, tympanitis, tympanoplasty, tympanum, tympanosclerosis
-TONIA/ -TONIC .... e.g.	tension	*isotonic (equal tension)*, hypertonia, hypotonia, normotonia

Prefix/ suffix	Meaning	Examples to practise
-TROPHY	nourish-ment	*dystrophy (defective nutrition)*, atrophy, hemiatrophy, hypertrophy
e.g.		
ULTRA- ..ᴗ..d	beyond	*ultraviolet light (used to treat skin conditions)*, ultramicroscopic, ultrasonic, ultrasonography, ultrasound
e.g. ᴗ		
UNI- ..ᴖ.......	one	*unicellular (consisting of one cell)*, unilateral, uni-ocular, uni-ovular, unipara
e.g.		
UR- ......ᴗ..ᴗ..	urine, urinary organs	*urinalysis (examination of urine)*, uraemia, urinometer, urobilin, urochrome, urogenital, urogram, urography, urolith, urologist, uroxanthin
e.g.		
URETER-	ureter, from kidney	*ureteritis (inflammation of ureter)*, ureterocolic, ureterocolostomy, uretero-ileal, uretero-ileostomy, ureterolith, ureterolithotomy, ureterostomy, ureterovaginal, ureterovesical
e.g.		
URETHR-	urethra, from bladder	*urethritis (inflammation of urethra)*, urethrocele, urethrography, urethrometry, urethroplasty, urethroscope, urethrostenosis, urethrotomy, urethrotrigonitis
e.g.		
UTER-	uterus	*uterine (pertaining to uterus)*, uteroplacental, uterorectal, uterosacral, uterosalpingography, uterovaginal, uterovesical
e.g.		
-URIA	urine	*acetonuria (excess acetone in urine)*, acholuria, adiposuria, albuminuria, alcoholuria, bacilluria, biliuria, cystinuria, dysuria, glycosuria, haematuria, nocturia, polyuria, proteinuria, pyuria
e.g.		
VACCIN-	vaccine	*vaccination (inoculation)*, vaccine, vaccinia, vaccinotherapy
e.g.		
VALV-	valve, fold	*valvoplasty (plastic operation on valve)*, valvotomy, valvulae, valvulitis, valvulotomy
e.g.		

Prefix/ suffix	Meaning	Examples to practise
VARIC-	dilated vein	*varicocele (dilation of veins of spermatic cord)*, varices, varicose, varicosity, varicotomy
e.g.		
VAS-	vessel	*vas-deferens (excretory duct of testis)*, vasa vasorum, vascular, vascularization, vasculitis, vasectomy, vasoconstrictor, vasodilator, vaso-epididymostomy, vasomotor, vasospasm, vasovagal
e.g.		
VEN-	vein	*venepuncture (insertion of needle in vein)*, venesection, venoclysis, venogram, venography, venous, venule
e.g.		
VENTRI-CULO-	ventricle	*ventriculoscope (instrument for examining ventricle)*, ventriculocysternostomy, ventriculography, ventriculostomy
e.g.		
VERMI-	worm	*vermicide (agent that kills worms)*, vermiform, vermifuge, verminous
e.g.		
VESIC-	bladder	*vesicle (small bladder)*, vesicant, vesicostomy, vesico-ureteric, vesicovaginal, vesiculitis, vesiculopapular
e.g.		
VULV-	vulva, covering	*vulvectomy (excision of vulva)*, vulvitis, vulvovaginal, vulvovaginitis, vulvovaginoplasty, vulvular
e.g.		
XERO-	dry	*xeroderma (dry skin)*, xerophthalmia, xerosis, xerostomia
e.g.		

MEDICAL WORDS AND THEIR GREEK AND LATIN EQUIVALENTS

Medical secretaries are sometimes confused to find that dissimilar words relate to the same part or area of the body. The answer lies in the derivation (origin) of the words, which are almost always taken from Latin or Greek. The following lists medical words commonly used in English and their Greek and Latin equivalents.

English	Latin	Greek
anus	ano-	proct-
before	pre-/ante-	pro-
bile	bili-	chol-
bone	oss-	osteo-
breast	mamm-	mast-
death	mor-	necro-
egg	ovo-	oo-
eye	ocul-	ophthal-
finger	phalanges	dactyl-
first	prim-	proto-
hair	pilo-	trich-
joint	artic-	arthr-
kidney	renal	nephr-
many	multi-	poly-
milk	lact-	gala-
mouth	os (oral)	stoma
mucus	muco-	myx-
night	nocte-	nyct-
single	uni-	mono-
strangle	angi-	strang-
tear	lacrim-/lachrym	dacryo-
testicle	testi-	orchi-
tongue	lingua	gloss-
tooth	dent-	odont-
vagina	vagin-	colpo-
vein	ven-	phleb-
vessel (blood)	vaso-	angi-
womb	uterus/utero-	metr-/hyster-

3 Abbreviations, Symbols, Homonyms and Plurals

SOME ABBREVIATIONS USED IN PRESCRIPTION WRITING

Abbreviation	Teeline	Latin	English
ac		ante cibum	before meals
aq		aqua	water
aq ad		aqua ad	water to desired quantity
aur		auristillae	ear drops
bd (or bid)		bis die	twice a day
c		cum	with
caps		capsula	capsule
crem		cremor	cream
dil		dilutus	dilute
ex aq		ex aqua	in water
garg		gargarism	gargle
gutt		gutta	drops (eyedrops)
liq		liquor	solution in water
lot		lotio	lotion
mane		mane	morning
mist		mistura	mixture
mitt		mitte	give
moll		molle	soft
narist		naristillae	nasal drops

Abbreviation	Teeline	Latin	English
neb		nebula	spray
nocte		nocte	night
oculent		oculentum	eye ointment
od		omni diem	once a day
om		omni mane	every morning
on		omni nocte	every night
pc		post cibum	after meals
prn		pro re nate	whenever necessary
qds (or qid)		quater in die	four times a day
Rx		recipe	take
stat		statim	at once
supp		suppositorium	suppository
tds (or tid)		ter in die	three times a day
ung		unguentum	ointment

MEASUREMENTS IN MEDICAL DOCUMENTS

Mass

kg (kilogram)   mg (milligram)

g (gram)   μg (microgram)

Volume

l (litre)   ml (millilitre)

Length

m (metre)   mm (millimetre)

cm (centimetre)   μ (micron)

Temperature

C (Celsius)..ϛ.............

Time

h (hour).....|..........   wk (week)......⤳......

Other units

kJ (kilojoule).ϛʲ...........   mEq per l (milliequivalents per litre)..ᶯʋʋʲ.

J (joule)...ʲ.............   mEq per g (milliequivalents per gram)..ᶯʋʋʲ.

kcal (kilocalorie)...ϛ...........   %vv (percentage volume in volume).%ʋʋ.......

mmHg (millimetre of mercury)..ᶯʲ.....   %wv (percentage weight in volume)..%..⤳...

IU (international unit)..ʲʋ..........   %ww (percentage weight in the whole)..%..⤳...

mmol per l (millimol per litre)

ᶯʋʲ..........⤳.........

SYMBOLS COMMONLY USED BY DOCTORS

Symbol	Meaning	Symbol	Meaning
♀	female	⧣	fracture
♂	male	℞	recipe
+ve	positive	∴	therefore
−ve	negative	∵	because
Rh−	rhesus negative	c̄	with
Rh+	rhesus positive	s̄	without
△	diagnosis	↑	upgoing

Symbol	Meaning	Symbol	Meaning
..⤓..........	downgoing	...⅟₅₂....	one week
..<..........	less than	...⅟₁₂......	one month
..>..........	more than	...⸳ᵢ.......	one dose
..⊙..........	pint	...ᵢᵢᵢ.......	three doses
..⅟ₙ.........	one day	...ᵢᵥ........	four doses
..⁵⁄ₙ.........	five days		

HOMONYMS AND DISTINGUISHING OUTLINES

There are a number of similar sounding words in medical terminology, and there are some words which, when written in Teeline without medial (middle) vowels, can be transcribed incorrectly. The following distinguishing outlines will help you to eliminate the possibility of such errors:

abrasion	*(outline)*	aberration, abortion	*(outline)*
addiction	*(outline)*	adduction	*(outline)*
areola	*(outline)*	aureola	*(outline)*
arthritis	*(outline)*	arteritis	*(outline)*
aural	*(outline)*	oral	*(outline)*
bile	*(outline)*	boil, bowel	*(outline)*
calcification	*(outline)*	classification	*(outline)*
callus	*(outline)*	callous	*(outline)*
caloric	*(outline)*	choluric	*(outline)*
carpus	*(outline)*	corpus	*(outline)*
cheilitis	*(outline)*	colitis	*(outline)*
cirrhosis	*(outline)*	psoriasis	*(outline)*
clinic	*(outline)*	clonic, colonic	*(outline)*

convulsion	convolution
cornea	corona
costatome	cystitome
cytolysis	catalysis
dilate	dilute
dilation	dilution
erasion	erosion
faces	faeces
fraction	friction
glands	glans
glucagon	glycogen
hypertension	hypotension
ileum	ilium
iron	urine
labial	labile
lactase	lactose
lesion	lotion
leucoma	leukaemia
lice	louse
lipaemia	lipoma
macroscopic	microscopic
measles	muscles
medial	middle
mucus	mucous
nose	knees
pallor	pillar

perineal.. ⟋⟍ ....

peroneal.. ⟋⟍⟍ ......

polyp... ⟍⟋ ....

pulp... ⟍⟋ ....

prescribe... ⟋e ....

proscribe. ⟋e⟋ ....

psychosis. ⟋ ....

sycosis.. ⟋ ....

radical. ⟋ ⟍ .....

radicle. ⟋ ⟍ ....

scirrhus. ⟋ ....

scirrhous.. ⟋ ....

separation.. ⟋ ....

suppuration.... ⟋ ....

serious...... ⟋ ....

serous... ⟋ ....

signs... ⟍ ....

sinus... ⟍ ....

sinews.. ⟍ ....

sinuous.. ⟍ ....

stroma................

struma................

testis................

testes................

thoracotomy.... ⟋ ....

tracheotomy................

tubal... ⟍ ....

tubule... ⟍ ....

tuberculosis................

tuberculous................

varicose... ⟍ ....

verrucose... ⟍ ....

vascular... ⟍ ....

vesicular.. ⟍ ....

vesicle... ⟍ ....

vesical..... ⟍ ....

viral..... ⟍ ....

virile... ⟍ ....

SINGULAR AND PLURAL

It is important that you distinguish between singular and plural endings. The following are examples of plurals in common use in medical terminology, together with suggested Teeline endings:

Singular			**Plural**		
-US	alveolus		**-I**	alveoli	
	anus			ani	
	bronchus			bronchi	
	fundus			fundi	
	nucleus			nuclei	
-A	ampula		**-AE**	ampulae	
	fibrilla			fibrillae	
	papilla			papillae	
	patella			patellae	
	vertebra			vertebrae	
-IS	analysis		**-ES**	analyses	
	centesis			centeses	
	diagnosis			diagnoses	
	pelvis			pelves	
	pubis			pubes	
-EX	apex		**-ICES**	apices	
	index			indices	
	cortex			cortices	

Singular				**Plural**		
-IX	calix			**-ICES**	calices	
	cervix				cervices	
	varix				varices	
-UM	bacterium			**-A**	bacteria	
	caecum				caeca	
	maximum				maxima	
	ovum				ova	
	sacrum				sacra	
-X	coccyx			**-GES**	coccyges	
	meninx				meninges*	
	phalanx				phalanges	
	salpinx				salpinges	

* See *Second Teeline Workbook: Revised Edition* page 26

-EN	foramen			**-INA**	foramina	
	rumen				rumina	

4 Medical Terms Written as Abbreviations or Initials

A great many medical terms are represented by abbreviations and initials. The Teeline initials should be written joined together, unless it is easier to write them separately. Two tiny lines should be written underneath the outline.

In some cases, abbreviations may have more than one meaning, and you should take care to interpret the correct meaning.

Once you are familiar with a medical term, you can use the abbreviation in your shorthand notes, but insert a line underneath the outline if the term is to be transcribed in full, e.g.

ECT.............., electroconvulsive therapy.............. *or*...............

AA	Alcoholics Anonymous		AJ	ankle jerk	
abd	abdominal		alb	albumin	
ACTH	adrenocorticotrophic hormone		alk	alkaline	
			ANC	Antenatal Clinic	
ADH	antidiuretic hormone		ANS	Autonomic Nervous System	
ADP	adenosine diphosphate				
A & E	Accident and Emergency		ant	anterior	
			AP	anterior–posterior	
AFB	acid-fast bacillus		APH	ante-partum haemorrhage	
agg	agglutination				
AHA	Area Health Authority		appl	appliance	
AHG	anti-haemophilic globulin		appt	appointment	
			ARM	artificial rupture of membranes	
AI	artificial insemination				
AID	artificial insemination by donor		ATP	adenosine triphosphate	
			ATS	anti-tetanus serum	
AIDS	Acquired Immune Deficiency Syndrome		A & W	alive and well	
AIH	artificial insemination by husband				

BBA	born before arrival/ baby born in ambulance	
BCG	Bacille Calmette Guerin (inoculation against TB)	
BDA	British Dental Association	
BI	bone injury	
BID	brought in dead	
BMA	British Medical Association	
BMJ	British Medical Journal	
BMR	basal metabolic rate	
BNF	British National Formulary	
BNO	bowels not open	
BO	body odour/ bowels open	
BP	blood pressure/ British Pharmacopoeia	
BPC	British Pharmaceutical Codex	
BRCS	British Red Cross Society	
BSR	basal sedimentation rate	
BW	birth weight	
C_1	first cervical vertebra	
ca	carcinoma	
CAT	computerised axial tomography	

CCF	congestive cardiac failure	
CCU	Coronary Care Unit	
CD	controlled drug	
CHC	Community Health Council	
CHD	congenital heart defect/ coronary heart disease	
CHO	carbohydrate	
chol	cholesterol	
CNS	central nervous system	
CO	Casualty Officer/ carbon monoxide	
co	complains of	
CO_2	carbon dioxide	
COD	cause of death	
COHSE	Confederation of Health Service Employees	
CPPV	continuous positive pressure ventilation	
CPS	cardio-pulmonary resuscitation	
creps	crepitations	
C & S	culture and sensitivity	
CSF	cerebro-spinal fluid	
CSOM	chronic suppurative otitis media	
CSSD	Central Sterile Supply Department	

CSU	catheter specimen of urine	
CT	coronary thrombosis	
CVA	cerebro-vascular accident	
CVP	central venous pressure	
CVS	cardio-vascular system	
Cx	cervix	
CXR	chest X-ray	
D_1	first dorsal vertebra	
D & C	dilatation and curettage	
DCP	District Community Physician	
DDA	Dangerous Drugs Act	
DDT	dichlor-diphenyl trichlorethane	
DHSS	Department of Health and Social Security	
DMT	District Management Team	
DN	District Nurse	
DNA	did not attend/ deoxyribonucleic acid	
DOA	dead on arrival	
DOB	date of birth	
DOT	died on table	
DPT	diphtheria, pertussi, tetanus	

DS	disseminated sclerosis	
DT	delirium tremens	
DU	duodenal ulcer	
D & V	diarrhoea and vomiting	
DV	domiciliary visit	
DVT	deep vein thrombosis	
DXR	deep X-ray	
DXRT	deep X-ray therapy	
EBM	expressed breast milk	
EBS	Emergency Bed Service	
ECG	electrocardiogram	
ECT	electroconvulsive therapy	
EDC	expected date of confinement	
EDD	expected date of delivery	
EEG	electro-encephalogram	
EMG	electromyogram	
EMU	early morning urine	
ENT	ear, nose and throat	
ERG	electroretinogram	
ESN	educationally subnormal	
ESR	erythrocyte sedimentation rate	
EUA	examination under anaesthesia	

FB	foreign body	
FBC	full blood count	
FBS	fasting blood sugar	
FH	foetal heart/ family history	
FHH	foetal heart heard	
FHNH	foetal heart not heard	
fib	fibula	
flex	flexion	
FMF	foetal movements felt	
FMNF	foetal movements not felt	
FPC	Family Planning Clinic/ Family Practitioner Committee	
FSH	follicle stimulating hormone	
FU	follow-up	
FUA	follow-up appointment	
GA	general anaesthetic	
GB	gall bladder	
Ge	gonorrhoea	
GCFT	gonococcal complement fixation text	
GI	gastro-intestinal	
G & O	gas and oxygen	
GP	General Practitioner	

GPI	general paralysis of the insane	
GravI	primigravida	
GSL	general sales list	
GSW	gun-shot wound	
GTN	glyceryl trinitrate	
GTT	glucose tolerance test	
GU	gastric ulcer/ genito-urinary	
gyn	gynaecology	
Hb	haemoglobin	
HCG	human chorionic gonadotrophin	
HH	home help	
HMC	Hospital Management Committee	
HO	House Officer	
HP	House Physician	
HPI	history of present illness	
HRT	hormone replacement therapy	
HS	heart sounds/ House Surgeon	
ht	height	
HV	home visit/ Health Visitor	
I	iodine	

Abbrev	Term	Shorthand	Abbrev	Term	Shorthand
I_{131}	radioactive isotope of iodine		L	left	
ICSH	interstitial cell stimulating hormone		L_1	first lumbar vertebra	
ICU	Intensive Care Unit		LA	local anaesthetic/ left atrium	
ID	intradermally/ intravenous drugs		lab	laboratory	
IH	inguinal hernia		lap	laparotomy	
IHD	ischaemic heart disease		lat	lateral	
IM	intramuscularly		LE	lupus erythematosus	
IP	in-patient		LFT	liver function tests	
IPPV	intermittent positive pressure ventilation		LGH	lactogenic hormone	
IQ	intelligence quotient		LH	luteinizing hormone	
ISQ	in status quo (without change)		LHA	Local Health Authority	
ITU	Intensive Therapy Unit		LIF	left iliac fossa	
IUCD	intra-uterine contraceptive device		LIH	left inguinal hernia	
IUD	intra-uterine death		LLL	left lower lobe	
IV	intravenously		LMC	Local Medical Committee	
IVI	intravenous infusion		LMP	last menstrual period	
IVP	intravenous pyelogram		LOA	left occipito-anterior	
IVU	intravenous urogram		LOL	left occipito-lateral	
IZS	insulin zinc suspension		LOP	left occipito-posterior	
JVP	jugular venous pressure		LP	lumbar puncture	
KJ	knee jerk		LSCS	lower segment Caesarean section	
			LSD	lysergic acid diethylamine	

LSH	lymphocyte stimulating hormone		ND	normal delivery	
LUL	left upper lobe		neg	negative	
LV	left ventricle		NG	new growth	
LVF	left ventricular failure		no	number	
LVH	left ventricular hypertrophy		NPU	not passed urine	
LWP	letter with patient		N & V	nausea and vomiting	
			NYD	not yet diagnosed	
MCH	mean corpuscular haemoglobin		OA	osteo-arthritis	
			obs	obstetrics	
MCHC	mean corpuscular haemoglobin concentration		O & G	obstetrics and gynaecology	
MCV	mean corpuscular volume		op	operation	
			OP	outpatient	
ME	myalgic encephalomyelitis		OPD	Outpatient Department/ Orthopaedic Department	
metas	metastases		OT	occupational therapy	
MI	myocardial infarction				
MMR	mass miniature radiography		PA	pernicious anaemia	
			Para I	primipara	
MO	Medical Officer		PBI	protein bound iodine	
MRC	Medical Research Council		PBU	Premature Baby Unit	
MSSU/ MSU	mid-stream specimen of urine		PC	private certificate	
			PCO	patient complains of	
MSW	Medical Social Worker		PCV	packed cell volume	
NAD	no abnormality detected		PD	pupillary distance/ pregnancy diagnosis	
NBI	no bone injury				

PET	pre-eclamptic toxaemia	
pH	acidity/alkalinity	
PH	past history	
PI	present illness	
PID	prolapsed intravertebral disc	
PM	post mortem	
PME	previous medical examination/ post mortem examination	
PMH	past medical history	
PML	permitted medicines list	
PN	postnatal/ percussion note	
PNC	Postnatal Clinic	
PND	paroxysmal nocturnal dyspnoea	
POM	prescription only medicine	
POP	prescription only preparation/ plaster of Paris	
PP	private patient	
PPH	post-partum haemorrhage	
PR	per rectal	
PSW	Psychiatric Social Worker	
PT	physiotherapy/ pulmonary tuberculosis	
PU	passed urine	

PUO	pyrexia of unknown origin	
PV	per vaginal	
R	right	
RA	rheumatoid arthritis/ right atrium	
RBC	red blood count	
Rh	rhesus factor	
RHA	Regional Health Authority	
RIF	right iliac fossa	
RIH	repair inguinal hernia/ right inguinal hernia	
RLL	right lower lobe	
RMO	Resident Medical Officer	
RNA	ribonucleic acid	
ROL	right occipito-lateral	
ROP	right occipito-posterior	
RQ	respiratory quotient	
RS	respiratory system	
RSO	Resident Surgical Officer	
RTA	road traffic accident	
RUL	right upper lobe	
SAS	see as necessary	
SB	stillborn	
SG	specific gravity	

sibs	siblings		vert	vertebrae
SLE	systemic lupus erythematosus		VI	virgo intacta
			vit	vitamin
SMR	sub-mucous resection		VV	varicose veins
SOB	short of breath			
			vx	vertex
staph	staphylococcus			
strep	streptococcus		WBC	white blood cell
SWD	short wave diathermy		WBCC	white blood cell count
			WCC	white cell count
T	temperature			
			WHO	World Health Organisation
T & A	tonsils and adenoids			
TB	tubercule bacillus/ tuberculosis		WL	waiting list
			WMA	World Medical Association
TCA	to come again			
TCI	to come in		WR	Wassermann Reaction
TFT	thyroid function tests		wt	weight
TPR	temperature, pulse and respiration		XR	X-ray
TSH	thyroid stimulating hormone		XX	normal female chromosome type
			XY	normal male chromosome type
URTI	upper respiratory tract infection			
UTI	urinary tract infection		YOB	year of birth
UVL	ultraviolet light			
VD	venereal disease			
VDRL	Venereal Disease Research Laboratory			
VE	vaginal examination			

5 Case Studies

The case studies in this chapter will give you the opportunity to become familiar with typing medical correspondence. They are set in the working situations of different branches and specialities. Passages can be copy-typed or dictated and transcribed and, for this reason, they have been counted in tens for dictation. When a new medical word occurs in a piece of correspondence it is included in the vocabulary section before the passage to enable you to practise it—after first making certain that you know the meaning of the word. Because of this vocabulary development it is better to work through the case studies in the order in which they appear. Some very long outlines have been shortened so that they may be written more quickly.

You will also find that the case studies become progressively longer and more difficult. The style and type of correspondence varies (i.e. some are very medical and formal and others quite 'chatty') so that you will gain experience of the differing ways of the medical personnel who will dictate to you at work.

Note: The drugs mentioned in the case studies have upper or lower case initial letters in accordance with S. J. Hopkins, *Principal Drugs* (Faber and Faber, 7th edition, 1983).

MEDICAL CORRESPONDENCE

In medical letters the patient's details are always used as a heading, although styles vary. For example, some employers like to have the patient's date of birth typed in full and others prefer just the age. Any patient references (e.g. after a hospital visit) must be quoted in full and these may be included in the heading or used as part of the reference. In the first case study the letters are set out in full but, in order to save space, subsequent studies contain the relevant details only in the information section at the beginning and you will need to insert them in the correspondence as you type.

In Europe and the USA anyone who receives a medical degree is called 'doctor', and this includes dentists and veterinary surgeons. This is not so in Britain where only physicians have this title and surgeons are referred to as 'Mr' or 'Miss'. This dates back to the fifteenth century when surgeons were not qualified doctors but barbers who, with their sharp razors, became very adept at surgery. Even the practitioners of specialised branches of surgery, such as ENT, ophthalmology, gynaecology and obstetrics, are not called 'doctor'. Nowadays, however, all physicians and surgeons have to obtain a basic surgical and medical degree before they can practise medicine.

On envelopes and the addressee section of letters great care must be taken to use the medical personnel's correct qualifications and title, although doctors who know each other and are writing in an informal way usually omit these.

In formal communications you should observe the following rules:

- Civil honours precede military honours, except the Victoria Cross, which takes precedence over all others, e.g. Sir Giles Russell VC KBE DSO FRCS
- Medical degrees take precedence over surgical degrees, and surgical over obstetrical qualifications, e.g. Mr G Russell MD FRCS MRCOG
- A surgeon's medical degree should always appear, e.g. Mr G Russell MD FRCS
- When postgraduate degrees are held (FRCP, FRCS, FRCOG, FRCPsych, FRCGP), qualifying degrees may be omitted, e.g. Mr G Russell MD BS FRCS becomes Mr G Russell MD FRCS
- University degrees take precedence over the qualifications of the Royal College which come before Diplomas and Certificates, e.g. Mr G Russell MD MSc FRCS DMR
- Upon being awarded the coveted and prestigious title Fellow of the Royal Society, a doctor omits all other qualifications but retains any civil or military honours, e.g. Prof G Russell OBE FRS
- Letters begin with the courtesy titles, Dr, Mr, Miss, Professor, etc. and end with the doctor's full title and position, e.g. G Russell MD FRCS, Senior Registrar to Mr C Scott *or* G Russell MD FRCS FRCOG, Consultant Gynaecologist

WORKING WITH AN ORAL SURGEON

Information

Consultant: Mr T I French MD MSc FRCS   Consultant Oral and Maxillo-facial
   Surgeon   Cumberland Infirmary   Carlisle   Cumbria CA2 3HY
General Practitioner: Dr M J Wood MB ChB   61 High Street   Scotby Village   Carlisle
   CA4 3BD
Patient: Mr Martin Andrews   22 Plashet Grove   Scotby Village   Carlisle CA4 8HA   DOB
   25.11.19—   Aged 47   *Hospital reference:* 897TIF

Vocabulary

analgesics......................, chronic......................, gingivitis......................, metronidazole......................,

mg......................, patient......................, prescribed......................, prn......................,

recurrent......................, tds......................, ulcers...................... .

The first letter is in the fully-blocked, open punctuation style.

3 March 19—

Mr T I French MD MSc FRCS
Consultant Oral and Maxillo-facial Surgeon
Cumberland Infirmary
CARLISLE
Cumbria   CA2 3HY

Dear Mr French

MR MARTIN ANDREWS   DOB 2[10]5.11.19—
22 PLASHET GROVE   SCOTBY[20] VILLAGE   CARLISLE CA4 8HA

Could you[30] please see this patient concerning soreness and recurrent ulcers and[40] spots in his mouth.

I have prescribed metronidazole 100[50] mg tds and advised him to take analgesics[60] prn. I feel he may be suffering from[70] chronic gingivitis.

Thank you for your help.

Yours sincerely

M[80] J Wood MB ChB   (*86 words*)

Vocabulary

bid......................, bilaterally......................, buccal mucosa......................, cervical......................, coalescing.. ...., Corsodyl. ...., diagnosis. ...., duodenal. ....,

dysphagia. ...., epilepsy. ...., gingivostomatitis. ....,

hard palate...... ...., herpetic (herpes). ...., intra-orally ...., ...,

lymphadenopathy. ...., malaise. ...., on examination (o/e)... ....,

phenobarbitone ...., quinsy... ...., renal. ...., symptomatic.................,

temperature........ ...., Zantac... ....

This letter is semi-blocked and fully punctuated.

18 April, 19—

Dr. M. J. Wood, M.B., Ch.B.,
61 High Street,
Scotby Village,
CARLISLE   CA4 3BD.

Dear Dr. Wood,

MR. MARTIN ANDREWS, D.O.B. 2[10]5.11.19— 897TI[20]F
22 PLASHET GROVE, SCOTBY VILLAGE, CARLISLE CA[30]4 8HA

Thank you for referring this patient[40] who was seen in our department 2 weeks ago. He[50] complained of generalised soreness throughout his mouth which was associated[60] with tender swellings on both sides of his neck. He[70] has noticed blisters and spots on his tongue, lips and [80] gums for some 6 days previously. This has coincided with[90] a general malaise and dysphagia.

I note that he suffers[100] from osteo-arthritis, epilepsy and was diagnosed as having a[110] duodenal ulcer in 1981. He also suffered from[120] quinsy in 1982. Presently he is being investigated[130] for renal stones. His current medication includes phenobarbitone 15 mg[140] tds, Zantac 150 mg bid[150] and metronidazole 100 mg tds, prescribed by[160] yourself.

On examination he had right sided cervical lymphadenopathy. Intra-[170]orally he had multiple coalescing ulcers on his tongue, lips[180] and right side of the hard palate and bilaterally in[190] his buccal mucosa. He also had chronic gingivitis and crusting[200] in his lower lip. His temperature had risen slightly to[210] 37.2 °C.

A diagnosis of primary[220] herpetic gingivostomatitis was made. The treatment at this later stage[230] was essentially symptomatic, therefore the patient was advised to use[240] Corsodyl mouthwash and analgesics prn. He was encouraged[250] to take as many oral feeds and fluids as possible.[260]

We arranged to see him again in 2 weeks' time,[270] when he failed to attend. We must assume, therefore, that[280] all is well and return the patient to your care.[290] If you would like me to see him again, please[300] do not hesitate to refer him.

Yours sincerely,   (*308 words*)

T. I. French, M.D., M.Sc., F.R.C.S.,
Consultant Oral and Maxillo-facial Surgeon

WORKING WITH A DENTAL SURGEON

Information

Surgeons: Mr R Davis BDS (Lond) 144–6 High Road Longdown Exeter Devon EX2
  5DW (NHS dentist)
Mr B Turnham BDS (Lond) 123 High Road Longdown Exeter Devon EX2 7FW
  (private dentist)
Patient: Mr David White 23 Buckholt Avenue Exeter Devon EX2 50N DOB
  28.12.19— Aged 51

These two dental practices co-exist happily on opposite sides of the busy High Road. The
surgeons are friendly socially and professionally and this is useful for both. In this case study
the patient is referred from the NHS practice to the private one because of alternative
anaesthetic options.
  Note: Teeth are counted from the front of the mouth, dividing in the middle for right and left,
i.e.

UR	UL
LR	LL

The two middle teeth in the front, upper jaw are 1| (upper right 1) and |1 (upper left 1), and the
two middle teeth in the lower jaw are 1| (lower right 1) and |1 (lower left 1). These symbols can
be made on the typewriter by using a raised underscore and the solidus (oblique) or one of
those characters and a matching pen.
  Therefore, some of the teeth mentioned in the letters are:
  6| lower right 6 (first molar)
  8| lower right 8 (wisdom)

Vocabulary

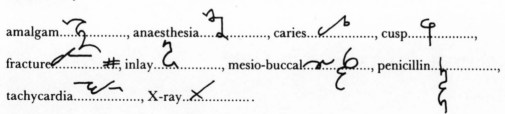

amalgam............., anaesthesia............., caries............., cusp.............,

fracture..........#, inlay............., mesio-buccal............., penicillin.............,

tachycardia............., X-ray............. .

From NHS dentist to private dentist (27 January 19—):

Dear Barry

I am enclosing the X-ray of the above[10] patient whom I asked you about at the Golf Club.[20] As I told you
then, I have recently completed a[30] long course of treatment for him, but on two occasions[40] I was unable
to achieve anaesthesia: first to fill lower[50] right 8 and then to repair the mesio-buccal cusp[60] of lower right
6.

I wonder whether the lower right[70] 8 ought to come out because I suspect the buccal[80] caries surrounding
the inlay is extensive and invasive. As far[90] as the lower right 6 is concerned, all I was[100] going to do was to
pin an amalgam into the [110] existing filling, thereby avoiding an anticipated fracture of the mesio-[120]buccal
cusp.

The patient's medical history is somewhat unclear – he[130] reports 'intermittent tachycardia' – and he is allergic to penicillin. He[140] seems quite well generally; indeed he gets up at 5[150] a.m. every weekday to commute to the other side[160] of the county.

I told him that you would contact[170] him either by phone or letter, and he perfectly understands[180] the system under which you operate.

Please give my best[190] wishes to Irene and I hope to see you both[200] soon.

Kind regards

Richard   (*204 words*)

Vocabulary

pontic..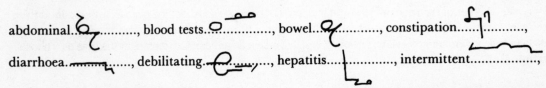

From private dentist to NHS dentist (1 March 19—):

Dear Richard

I have recently treated your patient as above[10] and am pleased to say the operation was successful and[20] anaesthesia obtained without any ill-effects. The fractured cusp from[30] the lower right 6   and the temporary filling in the[40] lower right 8   were removed and replaced with amalgam. I[50] also replaced the lost pontic facing.

Mr White has been[60] told to return to you for his routine treatment.

Best[70] wishes

Barry   (*72 words*)

WORKING WITH A GASTRO-ENTEROLOGIST

Information

Consultant: Dr Lyn Smithson MRCP   The Middlesex Hospital   Mortimer Street   London   W1N 8AA
General Practitioner: Dr A Abayoni MB BS   35 Hansford Crescent   London SW18 2CH
Patient: Mr Peter Overall   19 Danvill Street   London SW18 4BD   DOB 4.10.19—
   Aged 32   *Hospital reference:* 34/C/1068

Vocabulary

abdominal.............., blood tests.............., bowel.............., constipation..............,

diarrhoea.............., debilitating.............., hepatitis.............., intermittent.................., irritable bowel syndrome (IBS)* ...~~✺~~........, liver function...✑..✑...,

lymphocytosis...✑.............. .

* See Chapter 4 Medical Terms Written as Abbreviations or Initials (page 61).

From GP to Consultant Gastro-enterologist (10 November 19—):

Dear Dr Smithson

Thank you for seeing this patient who[10] is a catering officer at University College, London.

He has[20] had intermittent abdominal pain since a bad attack of hepatitis[30] in 1979. When he has the abdominal pain[40] he suffers from alternating diarrhoea and constipation. He also feels[50] symptomatically ill and weak, and this is the most debilitating[60] feature.

Recent blood tests show normal liver function and the[70] full blood count is normal, apart from a relative lymphocytosis[80] of 43.2%. He has tried[90] all the usual drugs and fibre products used for symptomatic[100] relief in irritable bowel syndrome but none have really helped.[110] He eats a high fibre diet.

I would be very[120] grateful for your help with diagnosis and management of this[130] patient.

Yours sincerely

A Abayoni   (135 words)

Vocabulary

biopsy...✑.............., Genito-Urinary Dept (GUD)...✑.............., homosexual...✑.......,

HTLV III (human T-cell lympho-trophic virus type 3)...✑.3........, infection...✑..........,

investigation...✑.........✑........, negative...✑............., sigmoidoscopy...✑..............,

symptoms..................., the examination...✑............. .

From Consultant Gastro-enterologist to GP (19 December 19—):

Dear Dr Abayoni

Thank you for referring this 32-[10]year-old single gentleman, who reports lower abdominal pain for[20] the past 3 months with frequent bowel action and formed[30] motions. His symptoms have improved greatly during the past few[40] weeks and bowel frequency is now between 1 and 3[50] times daily. He has lost around 2 kg in weight.[60]

Past medical history includes intermittent abdominal pain since the age[70] of 20 and what is described as 'a nervous bowel'[80] during his childhood. He had hepatitis B infection during 19[90]79.

He attends the Genito-Urinary Department regularly. He[100] told me that he is a homosexual and last year[110] was HTLV III negative. He lives alone[120] and has had one partner for the past 18 months.[130]

He appeared well. There was no rash or lymphadenopathy. The[140] remainder of the examination, which included sigmoidoscopy to 15 cm,[150] was normal. Biopsy was taken.

Although this gentleman's symptoms are[160] much improved in the past two weeks, I think investigation[170] is warranted, in particular exclusion of bowel infection. I shall[180] see him again in a few weeks.

Yours sincerely

Lyn[190] Smithson   *(191 words)*

Vocabulary

culture..�ↄ̣............., discharged...ᷗ............, microscopy....ᷗ..........., rectal..../......ᶜ....,

stool.....ᷗ........... .

From Consultant Gastro-enterologist to GP (25 February 19—):

Dear Dr Abayoni

This gentleman, whom you referred for investigation[10] of altered bowel habit, is now well, reporting no bowel[20] disturbance. Investigations have shown stool microscopy and culture is negative.[30] A rectal biopsy was normal. I have now discharged him[40] from the Clinic and re-assured him.

Yours sincerely

Lyn Smithson[50]   *(50 words)*

WORKING WITH AN OPHTHALMIC OPTICIAN

Information

Consultant: Mr J L Eastwood Ferrers MD FRCS   Inverclyde Royal Hospital   Larkfield
    Road   Greenock   Renfrewshire PA16 0XN
Ophthalmic Optician: Mr M J Revell FBOA (Hons) D Orph   41 Corringham
    Road   Kilmacolm   Renfrewshire PA13 5MZ
Patient: Mr John Coverdale   12 Roseberry Drive   Kilmacolm   Renfrewshire PA13
    6AS   DOB 10.12.19—   Aged 62   *Hospital reference:* JLEF 890621

All professions use abbreviations that puzzle the uninitiated. The medical profession is no exception. If you were working in a branch of oral medicine you would know that ⌊4 stands for 'upper left 4' and that it refers to a particular tooth. Similarly, in ophthalmics you would know to read the refraction paragraph of the letter below as 'right eye, plus 050 sphere minus 1 cylinder, axis 150 degrees, 6 over 12' and 'left, plus 050 sphere minus 1 cylinder, axis 75 degrees, 6 over 12'.

Vocabulary

acuities................., axis..✗........., cataracts................., distance..ᷗ..ᷗ....,

exophoria.✗......✗/....., lenses.ᷗ.............., lenticular.ᷗ............., oculomotor...ᷗ........., ophthalmoscopy..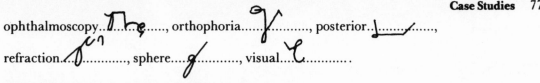....., orthophoria............., posterior............,

refraction..............., sphere............., visual................ .

From Optician to Consultant (12 March 19—)

Dear James

Report on:	Mr John Coverdale 12 Roseberry Drive Kilmacolm Renfrewshire PA13 6AS
Refraction:	R + 0.50 / −1.00 × 150 6/12 L + 0.50 / −1.00 × 75 6/12

Oculomotor Balance: Distance   Orthophoria

                      Near   3   Exophoria

Accommodation: Normal

Ophthalmoscopy: There is pronounced yellowing at the posterior poles of both lenses, and these lenticular cataracts are now affecting Mr Coverdale when working in his office. I recorded the corrected visual acuities of each eye as 6/12 and note that when I saw him last on 20 October last year this was recorded as 6/6 for each eye. Mr Coverdale would welcome your advice.

Yours sincerely

Michael

(*not counted*)

Vocabulary

abnormality..............., implant.............., intra-ocular.............., operation..............,

referral..............., subcapsular..............., vision................ .

From Consultant Ophthalmologist to Optician (18 April 19—):

Dear Michael

Thank you very much for your helpful referral[10] of this patient, who certainly has marked cataracts in both[20] eyes of the posterior subcapsular type which, as you know,[30] affects central vision fairly rapidly. There was no other abnormality[40] and I have recommended cataract operation for him, starting with[50] the right eye. He is keen to get on with[60] this fairly quickly.

I have provisionally arranged for him to[70] come in to the hospital on 21 April 19[80]— for right cataract operation with intra-ocular lens[90] implant.

Yours sincerely

James

(*94 words*)

Vocabulary

capsule...𝒸............, chamber........⤴............, laser....𝒸............, refract....𝒻............,

Yag...⤴............

From Consultant Ophthalmologist to Optician (11 June 19—):

Dear Michael

This very nice man had a right cataract[10] operation on 22 April 19— with a[20] posterior chamber intra-ocular lens implant. All has gone very[30] satisfactorily. A slightly thickened posterior capsule was treated with Yag[40] laser so there is a nice central gap now.

Would[50] you be kind enough to refract him any time from[60] early July? This will save him the journey to the[70] hospital as he is busy arranging a move to London[80] in the summer.

With all good wishes

Yours sincerely

James[90]   (*90 words*)

WORKING WITH A GYNAECOLOGIST

Information

Consultant: Miss J Miller MB FRCOG   Dudley Road Hospital   Birmingham B18 7QH
General Practitioner: Dr P Stanley MB ChB   20 St Dunstan's
    Avenue   Edgbaston   Birmingham B15 30E
Patient: Mrs Wendy Brown   233 Shakespeare Avenue   Edgbaston   Birmingham B15
    9WR   DOB 9.10.19—   Aged 27   *Hospital reference:* 01729GYN

Vocabulary

appointment...⌐............, basal...𝒷............, contraceptive.........⤳........., cycle...ℰ............,

erratic...⤫............, infertility...⤲............, menstrual.........𝒸.......

From GP to Gynaecologist (12 February 19—):

Dear Jean

The above patient came to see me yesterday[10] concerning 2 years of infertility. She was previously on the[20] contraceptive pill for about 3 years. Her menstrual cycle is[30] rather erratic, sometimes 5–7 weeks per cycle. I[40] have asked her to commence taking her basal temperatures and[50] to await an appointment with you.

Yours sincerely

Peter Stanley[60]   (*60 words*)

Vocabulary

analysis..........., Clomid............, ovulation............, semen............ .

From Gynaecologist to GP (29 May 19—):

Dear Peter

Thank you for referring this pleasant lady to[10] me. I saw her this morning in my Clinic and[20] she brought with her 3 months of basal temperature charts.[30]

As there is no clear sign of ovulation I have[40] commenced her on Clomid 50 mg for 5 days beginning[50] on day 3 of each cycle. She has been given[60] 3 months' supply and, in the meantime, I have asked[70] for a specimen of her husband's semen to be brought[80] to my Department for analysis.

Yours sincerely

Jean Miller

(89 words)

Vocabulary

hysterosalpingogram............, motility............, ovulating............,

prescribed............, Pro-Viron............, sperm............ .

From Gynaecologist to GP (20 August 19—):

Dear Peter

I have just seen this patient in my[10] Clinic again. The Clomid seems to have regulated her cycle[20] nicely and her temperature charts are showing a marked dip[30] and rise around days 13–14, so she seems[40] to be ovulating. Her husband's sperm count was a bit[50] low, 25 millions per ml with only 40 per[60] cent motility, so I prescribed Pro-Viron 25 mg[70]tds for him for a couple of months[80] to try to improve this.

I think the next step[90] is to bring her in as a day case for [100] a hysterosalpingogram and I will let you know the results[110] of this test in due course.

Yours sincerely

Jean Miller[120]

(120 words)

Vocabulary

bicornuate............, salpingogram............, uterus............ .

From Gynaecologist to GP (20 October 19—):

Dear Peter

A salpingogram performed last week on this patient[10] showed bilateral fill and spill, so this is not the[20] problem. Her uterus was slightly bicornuate but not enough to[30] cause her infertility.

I think we shall just carry on[40] with the Clomid and hope that the salpingogram has blown[50] the cobwebs away!

Yours sincerely

Jean Miller   (*57 words*)

Vocabulary

EMU (early morning urine specimen)................, period.................., pregnancy.................. .

From GP to Gynaecologist (1 December 19—):

Dear Jean

I saw this patient of ours yesterday and[10] she is now 6 weeks' overdue for a period. An[20] EMU has been sent for pregnancy testing to[30] the laboratory, although Wendy was so anxious that she has[40] used a home-testing kit which has already given a[50] positive reading.

I have asked her to come and see[60] me again next week and, in the meantime, to rest.[70] If she is pregnant it will certainly be a very[80] precious baby.

Yours sincerely

Peter Stanley   (*86 words*)

Vocabulary

9/40 (9 weeks' pregnant)................, antenatal................, approximately................ .

From GP to Gynaecologist (21 December 19—):

Dear Jean

The EMU has indeed come back[10] positive and an examination shows Wendy to be approximately $9^{20}/40$ pregnant. She is delighted and says it is[30] the best Christmas present she has ever had.

I am[40] referring her to you for her antenatal care so you[50] will see her again early in the new year. Thank[60] you for all your help.

Yours sincerely

Peter Stanley   (*69 words*)

WORKING IN PRIVATE MEDICINE

Information

There are several private medical insurance schemes in operation in the UK. The larger ones may build and run private hospitals and/or use private pay beds in NHS hospitals for their clients. One of the services that they offer is comprehensive health screening, which includes the 'well-woman screen'. This usually comprises routine blood, urine and cervical smear tests and a consultation with a doctor who performs a clinical examination of the breasts and pelvic area.

Physician in Charge: Dr A Bunyan MB BS MRCGP DRCOG   Private Medical
   Centre   Mountain Street   Mayfair   London W1 6OC

Vocabulary

adnexae................., axillary................., benign................., BP (blood pressure).................,

cervix................., fibro-adenoma................., fibrocystic.................,

glands................., LMP (last menstrual period)................., malignancy.................,

mammography................., microcalcification.................,

NAD (no abnormality detected)................., nodes................., nodularity.................,

normal................., palpable................., PR (per rectum)................., quadrant.................,

radiological................., stroma................., urine................., vagina.................,

vulva................. .

WOMEN'S SCREENING REPORT

NAME: Miss Alexandra Bolton   Yew Tree House   Brook Avenue   Kensington   London SW7 4DA
AGE: 49   **DOB:** 21.2.19—   **NO:** B010.643.891   **SEEN BY:** Dr A Bunyan
DATE OF VISIT: 3.5.19—   **SISTER:** S Malling
GENERAL PRACTITIONER: Dr L Hartswood MB   40 Prince Consort Road   London SW7 2BC

BREAST ASSESSMENT   o/e soft fibrocystic breasts with increased nodularity[10] in upper outer quadrants and lower outer quadrants. A small[20] nodule (well-defined, mobile) felt in right axillary tail and[30] another small nodule felt (also well-defined and mobile) in[40] left upper outer quadrant at breast margin – both consistent with[50] glands or fibro-adenoma. Bilateral axillary nodes palpable, soft, mobile[60] and not enlarged.

MAMMOGRAPHY   In the superior portion of the[70] left breast, a few flecks of microcalcification are noted.

These[80] are probably entirely benign but I would advise a careful[90] clinical follow-up in one year's time with further views[100] of this breast to note any untoward change. The stroma[110] of the right breast is a little nodular but there[120] is no radiological suggestion of malignancy within it.

GYNAECOLOGICAL ASSESSMENT[130]

LMP 1970   CYCLE AND LOSS nil   CONTRACEPTION/[140]OTHER HORMONES nil
o/e vulva /– normal
    vagina – normal
    cervix[150] – normal
    uterus – normal
    adnexae – difficult to feel
    per rectum – N[160]AD

GENERAL INFORMATION   HEIGHT 165 cm   WEIGHT[170] 50 kg   BP 120/70
URINE P[180]H6 NAD   BLOOD NAD   CHEST[190] X-RAY NAD

RECOMMENDATIONS   In view of breast clinical[200] findings a further check by Dr Hartswood would be advisable.[210]

SIGNED

Arnold Bunyan   (*213 words*)

Vocabulary

abscess.................., ankle jerk..................., appendix.............., artery.................,

blockage.............., bypass.............., cholecystectomy..............., circulation.............,

colonic............., excision..............., femoral..............., femur.............,

follicular............., fractured..............., groin............., hospital.............,

investigations..............., knee............., laparotomy.............,

lymphoma..............., major surgery...............,

medical (centre)..............., partial............., radiotherapy...............,

recurred............., re-examination..............., resection.............,

septicaemia............., strictures..............., thrombotomy................. .

Physician in Charge to GP (10 May 19—):

Dear Dr Hartswood

This patient of yours was seen here[10] on 3 May for a well-woman screen. She told[20] me her past history of a giant follicular lymphoma in[30] her groin, which was treated by excision at St George's[40] hospital in 1967 and then recurred in 19[50]69 while she was in New York. She then[60] had major surgery and radiotherapy and this resulted in nerve[70] damage to her leg, radiation damage to her bowel and[80] partial blockage of her femoral artery in the right leg.[90] In 1972 she had to have a laparotomy[100] and the removal of an appendix abscess. In 1971[104] she underwent resection of the small bowel and bypass[120] of colonic strictures. This was done at St George's hospital.[130] She also had a thrombotomy and suffered from septicaemia. In[140] 1975 she had a cholecystectomy and in 19[150]82 she fractured her left femur following a fall.[160] She has recently been feeling reasonably well although she does[170] get tired easily.

On examination she had weaknesses of both[180] legs, much more pronounced in the left leg with absent[190] knee and ankle jerks. Sensation was somewhat diminished on the[200] left. Circulation in both legs was rather poor. I enclose[210] a copy of the investigations that were done, and have [220] also sent a copy to Miss Bolton who requested them.[230] You will note her mammogram report and I suggest that[240] she comes to you for re-examination of her breasts.

Apart[250] from the above I found Miss Bolton remarkably fit considering[260] all she has gone through in the past. She does[270] smoke 25 cigarettes a day and I have suggested[280] to her that she tries to give up. I believe[290] she has already attempted to do so but now says[300] she is more determined than ever.

Please contact me if[310] you have any queries on the report.

Yours sincerely

A[320] Bunyan

(321 words)

Vocabulary

diagnosed........., examine............., on general examination............,

illnesses............, major operations............, nodules............, radiological

evidence.............

From Physician in Charge to patient – there is no need to include patient details (10 May 19—):

Dear Miss Bolton

It was a pleasure to meet you[10] here on 3 May. I now have the results of[20] your investigations.

You told me of the serious illnesses that[30] you have had since your giant follicular lymphoma was diagnosed[40] in 1967. I note that you have had[50] a number of major operations and have really been very[60] ill in the past. However, you have been much better[70] recently, although your legs are still very weak. You get[80] tired rather easily but otherwise you manage extremely well.

On[90] examination your breasts were noted to be somewhat lumpy, consistent[100] with benign nodules. Your chest was quite clear. I could[110] find no serious abnormalities on general examination. I noted the[120] weakness of your legs. As requested, I enclose a copy[130] of the investigations that were performed. You will note that[140] the mammogram report of your breasts shows some microcalcification of[150] the left breast but there is no radiological evidence of[160] malignancy. It is advised by the radiologist that you should[170] have a repeat mammogram in a year's time but I[180] also feel it would be wise for you to have[190] a further check by Dr Hartswood. Perhaps you would make[200] an appointment with him so that he can examine your[210] breasts again. The blood, urine, chest X-ray and all other[220] tests were satisfactory.

If you have any questions please do[230] not hesitate to get in touch. I would be pleased[240] to see you again in a year or so for[250] another check.

Yours sincerely

A Bunyan

(256 words)

WORKING WITH A GENERAL PHYSICIAN

Information

Consultant: Dr A L King MRCP   The London Hospital   Whitechapel   London E1 8NS
Registrar to Dr King: Dr H Hassan MRCP
General Practitioners: (1) Dr D Finchley MB ChB   Livingstone Street Health
    Centre   Livingstone Street   Limehouse   London E14 3HQ
(2) Dr S Gaskill MB BS   32 Brick Lane   Shoreditch   London E1 5NS
Dr Lee Chan MB LRCP   Senior Medical Officer   Her Majesty's Prison
    Wandsworth   Heathfield Road   London SW18 6DF
Patient: Mr John Preston (1) 8 Maybury Buildings   Atlas Street   London E14 5HN
    (2) 170a Brick Lane   London E1 7HL   DOB 20.4.19—   Aged 32   *Hospital
reference:* 85592 MNP   *Prison reference:* 82/C/24790

Vocabulary

discharge summary................., emergency................., out-patient................
From Consultant to GP (1) (20 April 19—):

Dear Dr Finchley

I have enclosed the discharge summary of[10] your patient, who was admitted here as an emergency on[20] 27 February, after being found collapsed at home. He[30] has been given an out-patient appointment for 2 months'[40] time.

Yours sincerely

A L King

(46 words)

Vocabulary

acid fast bacilli................., acidosis................., acidotic................., acute.................,

alcohol................., admission................., alkaline phosphatase................., ALT (alanine

aminotransferase)................., anorexic................., anti-tuberculous.................,

AST (aspartate aminotransferase)................., barium meal................., bicarbonate....................., bilirubin..................., blood count...................,

blood gases..................., cavitating..................., chemotherapy...................,

Chlordiazepoxide..................., clotting time..................., dehydration...................,

detoxification..................., EEG (electro-encephalogram)..................., electrolytes...................,

epigastric..................., epileptic..................., ethambutol..................., grand mal...................,

haematemesis..................., haemoglobin..................., Heminevrin...................,

infusion..................., intravenous..................., isoniazid...................,

jaundiced..................., lesion..................., lumbar puncture...................,

migraine..................., mmol/litre..................., Multivite..................., nocte...................,

pH..................., Phenytoin..................., pulmonary..................., resuscitate...................,

Rifampicin..................., secondary..................., seizures..................., sensitive...................,

sodium..................., spider naevi..................., sputum culture...................,

stabilised..................., streptomycin..................., temazepam...................,

TB (tuberculosis)..................., vomiting..................., urea...................,

WBC (white blood cells)....................

On the patient leaving hospital a Discharge Summary, detailing the treatment received, is prepared by the medical staff. One copy is placed in the patient's hospital notes and the other sent to the GP.

DISCHARGE SUMMARY

NAME OF PATIENT ....

AGE ....

DOB ....

NO ....

DATE 20.4.19—

ADDRESS ....

....

PHYSICIAN OR SURGEON ....

ADMITTED 28.2.19—   DISCHARGED 15.4.19—

INDEX DIAGNOSIS

1   acute lactic acidosis secondary to a high alcohol intake
2   pulmonary tuberculosis
3   epileptic seizures on withdrawing from alcohol

PATIENT'S GENERAL PRACTITIONER ....

ADDRESS ....

....

PAST HISTORY: Previous history of migraine. An EEG[10] at that time shows slow activity in the right side[20] of his head.

A year previously he had attended a[30] detoxification centre, but had apparently continued to drink alcohol despite[40] this initial withdrawal. Over the preceding year he had lost[50] a substantial amount of weight and over the 9 days[60] before admission he had been vomiting repeatedly, complaining of epigastric[70] pain and had been anorexic.

On the day of admission[80] these symptoms had worsened and he had a small haematemesis.[90]

TREATMENT HISTORY: No regular medication. High alcohol intake, both spirits[100] and beer. A smoker.

EXAMINATION: On admission he was acidotic,[110] dehydrated and wasted in appearance. He had spider naevi over[120] the upper abdomen but was not jaundiced. He had a[130] tachycardia of 120/min which was regular,[140] and abdominal examination revealed him to have a rigid, tense[150] abdomen, most markedly tender in the upper part. Rectal examination[160] revealed no specific abnormality.

INVESTIGATIONS: His initial blood gases revealed[170] him to have a pH of 7.16[180] and a bicarbonate of 4.0 mmol/litre.[190]

His urea and electrolytes appeared to be normal but his[200] sodium was reduced to 133 mmol/litre.[210]

A full blood count revealed a haemoglobin of 16.[220]8 and a WBC of 13.1.[230] His clotting time was normal.

Subsequent liver function tests revealed[240] him to have an elevated alkaline phosphatase, AST[250] and ALT but the bilirubin was normal.

A[260] chest X-ray showed him to have a cavitating lesion in[270] the left upper zone. Sputum culture for acid fast bacilli[280] was positive and he was fully sensitive to streptomycin, Rifampicin,[290] ethambutol and isoniazid.

MANAGEMENT: He was initially admitted and resuscitated[300] by giving intravenous fluid replacement and his acidosis corrected by[310] the use of intravenous bicarbonate. A barium meal was performed[320] in view of the history of haematemesis but this was[330] reported as normal.

Eight days after admission, when he appeared[340] to be well and mobile, he developed a series of[350] grand mal seizures, which were thought to be due to[360] the acute withdrawal from alcohol. These were eventually controlled on[370] a Heminevrin infusion.

He was subsequently converted to and stabilised[380] on Phenytoin. A lumbar puncture was performed during the acute[390] stage of his seizures and this was normal. In view[400] of the abnormality on his chest X-ray it was concluded[410] that he had pulmonary tuberculosis and he was commenced on[420] full anti-tuberculous chemotherapy. As shown above the sensitivities were[430] full to the medication used.

He was discharged home to[440] relatives when fully mobile and has been accepted to attend[450] a local detoxification centre.

Medication on discharge:

Phenytoin 100[460]mg tds
Rifampicin 300 2 tabs a[470] day
ethambutol 800 mg a day
Multivite 2 tabs[480] bd
Chlordiazepoxide 10 mg bd
temazepam 20 mg[490] nocte

He will be reviewed in 2 months.

SIGNED: A[500] L King   *(502 words)*

Vocabulary

clubbing......{..........., lactic..{............., pancreatitis..\.........

From GP (1) to Consultant (20 April 19—):

Dear Dr King

I gather that this patient was recently[10] treated under your care for lactic acidosis and pulmonary TB.[20] I have not yet had a full summary, but he[30] tells me that he also had pancreatitis and I wonder[40] if this is developing into a chronic state. I was[50] also slightly surprised to know that he had early clubbing.[60]

He is now complaining of early morning diarrhoea with pale[70] stools and epigastric pain radiating through to his back. He[80] looks much better kempt than previously and denies drinking, but[90] he does seem rather confused.

He tells me that he[100] has not received an out-patient appointment and I should[110] be grateful if you would send him one.

Yours sincerely[120]

D Finchley   *(122 words)*

Vocabulary

hypochondrium..ʰ.⌒.

From Registrar to GP (1) (16 May 19—):

Dear Dr Finchley

This young man with pulmonary tuberculosis and[10] alcoholism was seen earlier than anticipated and had unfortunately not[20] attended the detoxification centre. He complained of episodes of morning[30] diarrhoea, which have been a long-standing problem. Examination revealed[40] him to be tender in the left hypochondrium and rectal[50] examination was tender, but otherwise with no specific abnormalities. He[60] should continue taking his anti-tuberculous therapy, Rifampicin 300,[70] 2 tabs daily, and ethambutol 800 mg daily for[80] the next month whereupon, knowing the sensitivities of his infection,[90] it would be appropriate for him to discontinue the ethambutol.[100]

He will be seen again in 3 months' time, and[110] a chest X-ray will be available then.

Yours sincerely

H[120] Hassan
Registrar to Dr A L King   (*127 words*)

Vocabulary

amylase.............., barium enema................,

ESR (erythrocyte sedimentation rate)............, exophthalmic............,

malabsorption............, MCV (mean corpuscular volume)............,

melaena............, ova............, parasitic............, steatorrhoea................,

thyroid................ .

From Registrar to GP (2) (22 August 19—):

Dear Dr Gaskill

Thank you for your telephone call. I[10] apologise that you have not received further information about this[20] man with pulmonary tuberculosis and chronic alcoholism but, until you[30] have the case notes from his previous GP, the[40] enclosed copy of his discharge summary will provide some information[50] on his medical history.

When seen 3 months ago he[60] complained of abdominal pain and frequent bowel action which had[70] been present for some months. Blood tests were performed in[80] the last month which revealed a normal amylase, a haemoglobin[90] of 11.7 with an MCV of[100] 90 and an ESR of 5. His liver[110] function tests were normal, apart from a minimally elevated alkaline[120] phosphatase level of 120 units per litre, and[130] his urea and electrolytes were normal.

Clinical examination revealed him[140] to be thin and exophthalmic, but there was no palpable[150] thyroid present. Abdominal examination showed no specific areas of tenderness.[160]

He still complains of frequent bowel action, about 5 to[170] 6 times a day, but this does not appear to[180] be related to melaena or steatorrhoea. His weight is dropping[190] and he continues to smoke 40 cigarettes a day. I[200] think he may be describing symptoms of malabsorption and I[210] have arranged for a barium meal follow-through to be[220] performed because he was reluctant to consider a barium enema[230] at this stage. Stools have been sent for ova and[240] parasitic examination and thyroid function tests will also be done.[250]

He will be reviewed in a month's time.

Yours sincerely[260]

H Hassan   (*262 words*)

Vocabulary

anti-convulsant..............., disease..............., emaciated..............., excretion...............,

faecal..............., stigmata............... .

From Registrar to Senior Prison Medical Officer, copy to GP (2) (19 November 19—):

Dear Dr Lee Chan

This man was accompanied by a[10] prison warder today and has a year of his sentence[20] to serve. In a way, his detention is a good[30] thing as he no longer has access to alcohol. His[40] alcoholism can be considered to be cured and he assures[50] me that he will try not to return to his[60] old habits on his discharge from prison.

He is thin[70] but not emaciated and his weight has not changed in[80] the last 4 months, probably as the result of regular[90] meals. There are no stigmata or chronic liver disease. Chest[100] examination is normal and the chest X-ray is unchanged from[110] previously.

He has had 9 months' anti-tuberculous chemotherapy and[120] can now stop this. Although he has only had one[130] fit, and this was associated with alcohol withdrawal, he is[140] keen to continue with his anti-convulsant therapy and I[150] can see his point of view.

His recent faecal fat[160] excretion was normal which strongly militates against malabsorption.

His only[170] medication is Phenytoin 300 mg daily. Will you please[180] arrange for him to return here in 6 months.

Yours[190] sincerely

H Hassan   (*193 words*)

From Registrar to Senior Prison Medical Officer, copy to GP (2) (21 May 19—):

Dear Dr Lee Chan

This patient has now had a[10] complete course of therapy for his pulmonary tuberculosis and, 6[20] months after ceasing medication, he is gaining weight well. I[30] am also pleased to note that he has now abstained[40] entirely from alcohol. Mr Preston also feels that he can[50] discontinue the Phenytoin and so he is on no medication[60] whatsoever. I have not arranged to see him again.

Yours[70] sincerely

H Hassan   (*73 words*)

WORKING WITH A CARDIOLOGIST

Information

Consultant: Dr Michael Long FRCP   University Hospital of Wales   Heath Park   Cardiff
   CF4 4XW
Registrar to Dr Long: Dr Anna Theodopolis FRCP
General Practitioner: Dr William James MB ChB DCH   41 Beaumont
   Drive   Lisvane   Cardiff CF4 5XD
Patient: Mr David Johnson   21 Blackberry Side   Lisvane   Cardiff CF4 8BN   DOB
   8.7.19—   Aged 46   *Hospital reference:* 22587

Vocabulary

anterior................................., apex...................., atrial...................., cardiology....................,

cardiomegaly...................., cardiovascular system (CVS)....................,

CNS (central nervous system)...................., cyanosed...................., diastolic....................,

digoxin...................., dyspnoea...................., ECG (electrocardiogram)....................,

expiratory...................., fibrillation...................., haemoptysis....................,

JVP (jugular venous pressure)...................., kyphoscoliosis...................., mitral....................,

murmur...................., Navidrex K...................., nocturnal...................., oedema....................,

paroxysmal...................., paroxysmal nocturnal dyspnoea (PND)....................,

rheumatic...................., rhonchi...................., systolic..................... .

From GP to Consultant (15 January 19—):

Dear Dr Long

I should be grateful if you would[10] see this patient in your Cardiology Clinic. He is a[20] 46-year-old carpenter who presented to me on[30] 14 January 19—. He had rheumatic mitral valve [40] disease when he was 15 years of age. Five years[50] ago he was admitted to the Royal Hospital in Glasgow[60] with pulmonary oedema. For the past 5 months his exercise[70] tolerance has been about 200 metres on the flat[80] and he has been having recurrent attacks of dyspnoea at[90] night, most likely paroxysmal nocturnal dyspnoea.

A week before presenting[100] to me he developed a cough and a chest infection,[110] with more shortness of breath without chest pain or haemoptysis.[120] On examination he was slightly breathless, not cyanosed. His pulse[130] was 100 per minute in atrial fibrillation and his[140] blood pressure was 140/90. His J[150]VP was not raised and he had no ankle[160] oedema. Examination of the cardiovascular system revealed cardiomegaly, apex in[170] the sixth space in the anterior axillary line with a[180] diastolic thrill. There was a loud first sound, a short[190] systolic murmur and a rumbling mid-diastolic murmur. He also[200] has kyphoscoliosis to the right. There were a few expiratory[210] rhonchi and fine basal crackles at both bases. Examination of[220] the abdomen and CNS was normal. An ECG[230] showed atrial fibrillation at a rate of 110[240] per minute. His chest X-ray showed kyphoscoliosis and cardiomegaly. Full[250] blood count, urea, electrolytes and blood culture were normal.

I[260] have started him on digoxin 0.25 mg,[270] Navidrex K 2 tablets a day and a course of[280] antibiotics. I would be grateful if you could assess his[290] mitral valve disease. Thank you.

Yours sincerely

William James

(299 words)

Vocabulary

angina..............., angiogram..............., Cedocard retard...............,

coronary..............., exercise..............., Inderal LA..............., lymph nodes...............,

myocardial..............., od (once a day)..............., perfusion scan...............,

Thallium-201...............

From Consultant to GP (4 February 19—):

Dear Dr James

Thank you for referring this patient to[10] our Cardiology Clinic. For the past 3 weeks he has[20] been complaining of an angina-type pain, which has been[30] occurring most days and especially at night when he goes[40] to bed.

On examination he looked well and had a[50] blood pressure of 140/90. He was[60] slightly breathless but there was no cyanosis, clubbing or lymph[70] nodes. On direct questioning he says that he has not[80] had any haemoptysis or ankle oedema. Examination of the cardiovascular[90] system revealed cardiomegaly, a short systolic murmur and a mid-[100]diastolic murmur. A chest X-ray showed kyphoscoliosis to the right.[110] He still has a few expiratory rhonchi and fine basal[120] crackles at both bases. A full blood count was normal.[130]

I do not think this patient's mitral valve disease is[140] the problem here, but I consider that this angina-type[150] pain may be due to coronary disease. I have changed[160] his medication, therefore, to Inderal LA 160[170]mg od and Cedocard retard 20 mg bd.[180] I have also arranged an exercise test and Thallium-2[190]01 myocardial perfusion scan, after which he will be[200] seen again in the Clinic when we can reassess the[210] situation and decide whether or not an angiogram will be[220] needed.

Yours sincerely

Michael Long

(225 words)

Vocabulary

angiography..............., infero-posterior..............., propranolol...............,

protocol..............., scan..............., troublesome..............., vessel ....

From Registrar to GP (18 February 19—):

Dear Dr James

This man was reviewed in the Cardiology[10] Clinic today. Since commencing propranolol he has had only 2[20] episodes of chest tightness and feels much better.

He did[30] a good exercise test, stopping at stage 4 of our[40] protocol. At peak exercise there were infero-posterior changes in[50] the ECG and a corresponding defect in the Thallium scan[60] with slight improvement after redistribution. These changes suggest single vessel[70] disease and I think we should only advise coronary angiography[80] for symptoms which persist despite having full medical treatment.

He[90] should continue on propranolol long-acting 160 mg[100] od and Cedocard retard 20 mg bd. He[110] must, of course, stop smoking and he will be reviewed[120] again in 4 months. Should this pain remain troublesome I[130] would be happy to see him sooner.

Yours sincerely

Anna[140] Theodopolis

(*141 words*)

Vocabulary

amiloride........., amiodarone........., apical........., arrhythmias.........,

cardiac........., catheterisation........., circumflex.........,

consciousness........., diuretics........., frusemide........., infarction.........,

Isordil........., occlusion........., prognosis........., proximally.........,

qds (4 times a day)........., sinus rhythm........., stenosis.........,

tocainide........., vasodilators........., ventricular.........

From Registrar to GP (11 June 19—):

Dear Dr James

This gentleman was admitted as an emergency[10] on 21 May after suffering a myocardial infarction. Cardiac[20] catheterisation 3 days after admission showed occlusion proximally of the[30] left anterior descending and right coronary artery. He had a[40] tight proximal stenosis in the circumflex. Left ventricular function was[50] severely compromised.

He had a very stormy course, complicated mainly[60] by recurrent ventricular arrhythmias. This was eventually controlled on amiodarone,[70] and he was discharged on 30 May, only to be[80] re-admitted 2 days later with 2 episodes of loss of[90] consciousness at home. During this second admission he again had[100] recurrent ventricular tachycardia, which was eventually controlled with a combination[110] of tocainide and amiodarone, and his heart failure responded to[120] vasodilators and diuretics.

I reviewed him in the Clinic before[130] his discharge again today and he is feeling better, with[140] no further episodes of loss of consciousness or chest pain.[150] He has not been able to move as quickly as[160] he could before but says things seem to be getting[170] better.

On examination there were no signs of fluid overload.[180] He was in sinus rhythm with a blood pressure of[190] 110/80. There was a soft apical[200] third sound and clear lung fields. He should now take[210] Isordil 40 mg qds, tocainide 400 mg[220] qds, amiodarone 200 mg od, frusemide[230] 40 mg od and amiloride 5 mg od.[240]

Mr Johnson is stable at present, but unfortunately we cannot[250] be very hopeful about his long-term prognosis. He will[260] be reviewed again in one month.

Yours sincerely

Anna Theodopolis[270]

(*270 words*)

Vocabulary

allergies. ⌇ ...., anaemia. ⌇ ...., asymptomatic ...., blackouts.. ⌇ ....,

complications. ⌇ ...., CCU (Coronary Care Unit)... ⌇ ...., DC cardioversion (a

method of terminating abnormal heart rhythm by using electrodes and an electrical

discharge) ⌇ ...., ectopics..... ⌇ ...., intercostal.......... ⌇ ...,

myocardial infarction (MI) ⌇ ...., orthopnoea..... ⌇ ...., palpitations.. ⌇ ....,

precipitated.. ⌇ ...., wheezes...... ⌇ ....

Hospital summary (copy to GP):

MEDICAL IN-PATIENT SUMMARY

PATIENT .... HOSPITAL NUMBER ....

ADDRESS ....

CONSULTANT ....

GP .... DATE OF BIRTH ....

ADMITTED 25.9.19—   DISCHARGED 11.10.19—

DIAGNOSIS AND ANATOMICAL SITE Ventricular arrhythmias

HISTORY: This 47-year-old man was admitted on[10] 25 September. He is known to this hospital and[20] was on tocainide for ventricular arrhythmias, which complicated a myocardial[30] infarction in June of this year. He had 3 blackouts[40] in the preceding 6 days before his admission and had[50] felt dizzy and mildly short of breath before losing consciousness.[60] His loss of consciousness lasted for about one minute and[70] he felt slightly weak when he came round. He denied[80] any palpitations and there was no history of chest pain,[90] orthopnoea, PND or ankle swelling. He said that[100] he had not been regularly taking his dose of tocainide[110] as he had been feeling so well.

PAST MEDICAL HISTORY:[120] Myocardial infarction in June of this year complicated by ventricular[130] arrhythmias. This required DC cardioversion and treatment with amiodarone[140] and tocainide.

Pulmonary oedema 5 years ago – admission to Royal[150] Hospital, Glasgow.

FAMILY HISTORY: Nil of note.

SOCIAL HISTORY: Married[160] man with 2 children. He works as a carpenter. He[170] does not smoke now and drinks only occasionally. There are[180] no known allergies.

DRUGS ON ADMISSION:

Isordil 40 mg q[190]ds

    tocainide 400 mg qds
    amiodarone[200] 200mg od
    frusemide 40 mg od[210]
    amiloride 5 mg od

ON EXAMINATION: He looked well.[220] There was no cyanosis, clubbing, lymph nodes, jaundice or anaemia.[230] In the CVS the blood pressure was 11[240]0/70, pulse 80 per minute regular with ectopics,[250] although the volume was variable and became weak at times.[260] The JVP was not raised and heart sounds[270] one and 2 plus 0. The apex was displaced at[280] the seventh intercostal space mid-axillary line. All pulses were[290] present and there was no oedema. In the chest there[300] were a few scattered wheezes on both sides. The liver[310] edge was just palpable. CNS – normal. A chest[320] X-ray revealed evidence of an old MI and signs[330] of kyphoscoliosis.

PROGRESS DURING ADMISSION: Mr Johnson was admitted to[340] the CCU for observation and monitoring. It was[350] thought that his symptoms were due to recurrent ventricular tachycardia[360] precipitated by his not taking his tocainide. Rhythm strips while[370] in the Cardiac Unit showed short runs of ventricular tachycardia,[380] during which time he was asymptomatic. His tocainide was recommenced[390] and reduced to tds dosage.

On 7 October[400] a 48-hour tape showed runs of ventricular tachycardia.[410] His amiodarone level, while on 200 mg od,[420] had been 0.6, which is at the lower[430] end of the therapeutic range, and the amiodarone was, therefore,[440] increased to 200 mg bd.

On 11 October[450] he had a further 24-hour tape which showed[460] only a few runs of ventricular tachycardia, 3–4[470] beats maximum at a time, and occasional ventricular ectopics. He[480] remained asymptomatic during this, and his control was far improved[490] from that on admission.

He was, therefore, discharged home and[500] will be seen in the Out-patient Clinic in 2[510] months.

DRUGS ON DISCHARGE:

    Isordil 40 mg qds[520]
    tocainide 400 mg tds
    amiodarone 200[530]mg bd
    frusemide 40 mg od
    amiloride 5[540]mg od

SIGNED: Anna Theodopolis   (*546 words*)

From Consultant to GP (20 December 19—):

Dear Dr James

I saw this patient in the Clinic[10] today and he has made a remarkable recovery since his[20] last visit to us in October. He is now able[30] to walk a considerable distance before getting short of breath[40] and says that he feels much better on his new[50] dose of tocainide and amiodarone.

On examination today his blood[60] pressure was 110/75 and his[70] heart rate was normal. I have, therefore, discharged him back[80] to your care, but would be very happy to see[90] him in the future should you think it necessary. Mr[100] Johnson was happy with this arrangement.

Yours sincerely

Michael Long[110]   (*110 words*)

Vocabulary

auscultation... ⌒Ɛ ⁿ ...., lung... C.\ ....

From Registrar to GP (8 July 19—):

Dear Dr James

I was pleased to see Mr Johnson[10] in the Clinic today. He is doing quite well, although[20] he has not been out of the house much recently.[30] There is no shortness of breath while pottering about, he[40] can lie flat, and there has been no ankle oedema.[50]

There is no sign of fluid retention and his venous[60] pressure is normal. There is a soft third sound on[70] auscultation of the chest and clear lung fields. He is[80] doing so well that I am reluctant to reduce any[90] of his medication. He should remain on Isordil 40 mg[100] qds, tocainide 400 mg qds,[110] amiodarone 200 mg bd, frusemide 40 mg o[120]d and amiloride 5 mg od.

I will see[130] him again in 6 months' time.

Yours sincerely

Anna Theodopolis[140]

(140 words)

WORKING WITH A GENERAL PRACTITIONER

Information

General Practitioner: Dr Alan French MB ChB DCH   27 Thornbush
  Way   Basildon   Essex SS16 4PH
Consultant Paediatrician: Dr Arnold Rochelle MD FRCP   Basildon
  Hospital   Nethermayne   Basildon   Essex SS16 5NL
Consultant Orthopaedic Surgeons: Mr Robert Penny MB FRCS   Basildon Hospital
  Miss Jennifer Sefton MB FRCS   The Hospital for Sick Children   Great Ormond
  Street   London WC1N 3TH
Patient: Baby Claire Mortimer   22 Leinster Road   Basildon   Essex SS16 1VW   DOB
  7.12.19—   Aged 5 days   *Basildon hospital reference:* 12/281084   *London hospital reference:*
  E0030 34497

Vocabulary

consultant.. ⌒ ...., delivery .~~ ...., fracture ╱ .... #., full-term. ℓ ⌒ .....,

maternity ....~⌐ ...., osteogenesis imperfecta congenita (OIC)... Ɛ ....,

paediatrician.. ⌊⌐ ...., skeletal... Ɛ⌐ ...., surgeon. ⌐⌐ ...., unit ....,

wormian. ~⌐ ....

From Consultant Paediatrician to GP (14 December 19—):

Dear Dr French

You will doubtless recognise Mrs Mortimer as[10] one of your patients and, indeed, you carried out her[20] antenatal care. Her baby was born as a full-term[30] normal delivery in our Maternity Unit where it was found,[40] immediately after birth, that she had a fracture of the[50] right femur. Skeletal survey subsequently showed her to have other[60] fractures and wormian bones of the skull.

We must, unfortunately,[70] make the diagnosis of osteogenesis imperfecta congenita and I have[80] asked Mr Penny, Consultant Orthopaedic Surgeon at this hospital, to[90] undertake her follow-up. He will be writing to you[100] shortly.

Yours sincerely

A Rochelle   (*105 words*)

Vocabulary

humerus...⌐......ᴀ.........

From Mr Penny to GP (11 January 19—):

Dear Alan

In the Clinic today I reviewed this baby[10] who had a fracture of the right femur during delivery.[20] Skeletal survey has shown a fracture of the left femur[30] and the right humerus. She also has wormian bones.

Undoubtedly[40] this child has osteogenesis imperfecta congenita. There is no family[50] history of this and, in any case, it is usually[60] sporadic. The outlook has been explained to the parents and[70] we will obviously keep her under very careful review.

I[80] will be seeing the child again in 6 weeks' time[90] but if there are further fractures in the meantime I[100] would like to see her as soon as possible. If[110] you agree I think I will re-refer Claire to a[120] colleague of mine, Jennifer Sefton, at Great Ormond Street. They[130] have very good counselling facilities there for families of these[140] children.

I hope to see you at the meeting next[150] Tuesday evening.

Kind regards

Bob   (*155 words*)

Vocabulary

Brittle Bone Society.............., gallows traction.................,

spontaneous.............., vertex............., Wolfson Institute.................

From Mr Penny to Miss Sefton, copies to GP and Paediatrician (1 March 19—):

Dear Miss Sefton

I would be grateful if you could[10] see this baby in your Out-patient Clinic. She was[20] born by spontaneous vertex delivery and, in the process, her[30] right femur was fractured. Subsequently it became apparent that she[40] had a fracture of the left femur and right humerus.[50] X-rays show that she also has wormian bones of the[60] skull. In order to save you some time I have[70] enclosed all the X-rays taken at this hospital. Her initial[80] treatment here was gallows traction and subsequently she was put[90] in plaster.

Although there is no family history, she would[100] appear to have osteogenesis imperfecta congenita. Her parents have already[110] contacted the Brittle Bone Society, and someone from the Wolfson[120] Institute at your hospital has already visited them. They are[130] anxious for review at Great Ormond Street and I would[140] be grateful if you could see them and their baby.[150]

I have arranged to see Claire again in 3 months'[160] time, but obviously if you wish to take over her[170] care completely I would be delighted for you to do[180] so.

Yours sincerely

R Penny

(*185 words*)

Vocabulary

occupational.............., therapist.............. .

From Miss Sefton to Mr Penny, copies to GP and Paediatrician (9 March 19—):

Dear Mr Penny

Thank you very much for your letter[10] about this child. I would be very happy to see[20] her in our special Osteogenesis Imperfecta Clinic.

The person who[30] visited the parents was Anne Cambridge, an occupational therapist, who[40] runs the clinic at the Wolfson Centre. She is very[50] experienced in this type of case and the family are[60] in good hands.

I will write to you again after[70] I have seen Claire.

Yours sincerely

Jennifer Sefton

(*78 words*)

Vocabulary

femora. ⌒...⋏.......

From Mr Penny to GP (14 May 19—):

Dear Alan

I reviewed this little girl who has O[10]IC in the clinic today. I am glad to[20] say the femora are remodelling nicely, but there is some[30] bowing which I will query with Miss Sefton. I have[40] to telephone her tomorrow about another patient and I will[50] do it then.

I have not made a definite appointment[60] to see the child again but, obviously, if there are[70] further fractures or any other problems I have asked the[80] mother to come back and see me at any time.[90]

I hope you and Mavis are well.

Yours sincerely

Bob[100]

(100 words)

Vocabulary

intractable................., pneumatic................., re-rod................., rodding................. .

From Miss Sefton to Mr Penny, copies to GP and Paediatrician (31 May 19—):

Dear Mr Penny

Thank you very much for asking me[10] to see this baby with osteogenesis imperfecta congenita at the[20] special clinic held at the Wolfson Centre.

Basically she has[30] done very well following treatment for her fractures after birth.[40] There are no problems at present. She may be a[50] candidate for a pneumatic suit when she starts to get[60] on her feet, but I am not sure at the[70] moment. From my point of view, I would like to[80] see her again in about 6 months' time.

In the[90] meantime, I should be very happy if you would keep[100] an eye on her and treat any fractures locally. I[110] am sure you will appreciate that it is very difficult[120] for us to treat fractures here if the children live[130] a long way away.

Finally, with regard to the bowing[140] of the femora. I would not worry about this for[150] the time being because if I consider correction at this[160] point then I would probably have to re-rod within 6[170] months to a year. Therefore, I would only consider rodding[180] if Claire were having intractable recurrent fractures at this early[190] stage.

With best wishes

Jennifer Sefton

(196 words)

Vocabulary

condition.............., dominant.............., inactive.............., passive.............,

physical.............., stimulate..............

From Paediatrician to GP, copy to Miss Sefton (10 June 19—):

Dear Dr French

I saw this baby with osteogenesis imperfecta[10] congenita today. She is 6 months' old. Great Ormond Street[20] have done a good job in tracking down the history[30] and they feel that this is a mild, dominant condition.[40] Father's father had quite a lot of trouble; he used[50] to break his bones very easily as a child and[60] so was not able to play sport at school. Otherwise,[70] he seemed to do well. Father has only had 2[80] fractures in his life, so I hope the outlook for[90] Claire will also be good. It is very encouraging that[100] she has, so far, had no further fractures since birth.[110]

She remains a very inactive baby. She is still a[120] bit floppy and makes only the slightest attempt to help[130] pull up to sit, but her back is almost straight.[140] She has not yet any balancing reaction and she is[150] not weight-bearing. Part of this may very well be[160] because of the parents' understandable fear of encouraging her to[170] move or indulging in the normal physical play that most[180] babies receive. Perhaps now that they feel more confident that[190] she will not break any bones very easily, they will[200] be able to stimulate her more and encourage her to[210] get going.

I also feel that she is a very[220] passive child and may be a bit slow. I will[230] continue to watch her with this in mind. I am[240] planning to see her again in 3 months.

Yours sincerely[250]

A Rochelle

(252 words)

From Paediatrician to GP, copy to Miss Sefton (3 October 19—):

Dear Dr French

I saw this infant, who is now[10] aged 10 months and who has OIC.

I[20] am delighted that she has had no fractures, apart from[30] those that occurred at birth, even though she is now[40] crawling and becoming much more active than previously. Of course,[50] during the next few months she will commence walking and[60] it is highly probable that she might sustain a few[70] more fractures. It would be a good idea if I[80] kept an eye on her in the Out-patient Clinic[90] and I have asked to see her again in April[100] next year.

Yours sincerely

A Rochelle

(106 words)

Vocabulary

admitting.............., copious.............., dehydrated.............., diabetes mellitus........, glucose........, laboratory........,

presented........, respiration........, serum........ .

From GP to Paediatrician – taken to the hospital by Mrs Mortimer (12 June 19— – following year):

Dear Dr Rochelle

Thank you for admitting this child urgently.[10] She is, as you know, a case of osteogenesis imperfecta[20] congenita who is being followed up by yourself and Mr[30] Penny in your respective Out-patients.

She presented in surgery[40] today with a 3-day history of thirst associated with[50] the passage of copious quantities of urine.

On examination, I[60] found her to be dehydrated, hot and flushed with a[70] rapid respiration. Examination of all systems appeared to be normal[80] and an urgent blood sugar was requested at the laboratory.[90]

The result of the serum glucose was 34.[100]1 mmols per litre. This confirms the diagnosis of diabetes[110] mellitus.

Yours sincerely

Alan French   (*115 words*)

Vocabulary

act rapid insulin........, Monotard........, our ward........,

regime........, syringe........ .

From Paediatrician to GP, copy to Miss Sefton (18 June 19—):

Dear Dr French

Thank you for sending us this unfortunate[10] young lady who has had a lot to contend with[20] in her young life.

I agree with your diagnosis of[30] insulin dependent diabetes. She was treated with emergency insulin regime[40] upon admission to our ward and gradually stabilised, so that[50] she is now taking act rapid insulin, 2 units, and[60] Monotard insulin, 8 units, mixed in the same syringe once[70] a day.

She appears to be well stabilised on this.[80] The parents have been trained to give the insulin and[90] test the urine, though they are not yet confident about[100] testing the blood sugar. I am sure their confidence will[110] increase in time as they learn to handle Claire's illnesses.[120]

I will, of course, be following her up regularly in[130] the Out-patient Clinic.

Yours sincerely

A Rochelle   (*138 words*)

WORKING WITH AN ORTHOPAEDIC SURGEON

Information

Consultant: Miss Jennifer Sefton MB FRCS   The Hospital for Sick Children   Great Ormond Street   London WC1 3TH

Senior Orthopaedic Registrar: Mr Glynn Bates MB FRCS

Senior House Officer: Mr D R Grace MB MRCS

Paediatrician: Dr Bijan Fazeli FRCP   The William Harvey Hospital   Kennington Road   Willesborough   Ashford   Kent TN24 01Z

General Practitioner: Dr Graham Webb MB   The Surgery   Hawkswood Road   Ashford   Kent TN24 3FR

Patient: Jamie Wood   6 St Egbert's Terrace   Willesborough   Ashford   Kent TN24 9LK   DOB 7.12.19—   Aged 11 days   *Kent hospital reference:* 656091   *London hospital reference:* E 0045 18969

Vocabulary

A Rh +ve............, adducted............, Apgar............, breech............, cleft palate............, dislocated............, dysgenesis............, hare lip............, hypoplasia............, LSCS (lower segment Caesarean section)............, maldevelopment............, maternal............, miscarriage............, SB (stillborn)............, spina bifida............, TEV (talipes equinovarus)............, vertebral............ .

Note: Before dictating the following letter relevant dates should be inserted in the 'Maternal history' section to aid comprehension.

From Consultant Orthopaedic Surgeon to Consultant Paediatrician (18 December 19—):

Dear Miss Sefton

Thank you for taking the above patient[10] with spinal dysgenesis, small pelvis, short legs, adducted dislocated hips,[20] bilateral TEV, and no spontaneous or induced movements of[30] the lower limbs.

Birth history: LSCS for[40] breech presentation. Apgar scores – 6 at 1 minute, 8 at[50] 5 minutes. Birth weight – 3.1 kg; head circumference[60] – 37 cm.

Maternal history: 30 years   A Rh +ve[70]
19— – 8/40 miscarriage
19—[80] [following year] – 12/40 miscarriage
19—[same year] – 36/[90]40 SB bilateral hare lip and cleft palate
19—[100] [7 years later] – full-term female live birth
Smokes 10 per day. Normal[110] pregnancy.

Infant history:

Day 5 – Hb 21.2,[120] WBC 17.9

Day 9 – Hb 20[130].1, WBC 7.0

Spinal X-ray[140] – there is maldevelopment of the spine extending from D7[150] to L5. It consists of absence and hypoplasia of[160] the vertebral elements, both anterior and posterior. There is also[170] some spina bifida.

Thank you for your help.

B Fazeli[180]

(*180 words*)

Vocabulary

anomalies......✐........., dysraphism......✐........., flail......✐........., gait......✐.........,

General Surgeon......✐................., geneticists......✐............., gestation......✐.........,

hernia......✐........., herniotomies......✐........., inguinal......✐......, kyphosis......✐.........,

orchidopexy......✐..........., postero-medial......✐................, talipes......✐........... .

Note: Before dictating the Discharge Summary relevant dates should be inserted to aid comprehension.

Summary, copies to Paediatrician and GP:

DISCHARGE SUMMARY

NAME .... REFERENCE NO ....

ADDRESS ....

DATE OF BIRTH .... WARD Sunshine

ADMITTED 19.12.19—   DISCHARGED 12.1.19—

GP ....

REFERRING HOSPITAL ....

DIAGNOSIS

1   severe spinal dysraphism; 2   bilateral dislocated hips; 3   bilateral talipes equinovarus;
4   flail lower limbs.

HISTORY

The maternal pregnancy had been essentially normal. Delivered by[10] elective lower segment Caesarean section for breech presentation at 40[20] weeks' gestation. Birth weight 3.1 kg. Mother had[30] 2 previous miscarriages and a stillborn in 19—[40] by a previous marriage, and a healthy female child in[50] 19— by her present husband.

ON EXAMINATION

The[60] child was noted to have severe spinal anomalies centred on[70] the upper lumbar spine with virtually flail legs. The hips[80] were held in external rotation and adduction. Knees were rather[90] stiff, flexing from 10 to 90 degrees. There was gross[100] bilateral talipes equinovarus. He also had bilateral inguinal hernias.

PROGRESS[110]

He was seen by the General Surgeon who did bilateral[120] inguinal herniotomies and a right orchidopexy. The geneticists were also[130] asked to see him and felt that he did not[140] have any particular developmental syndrome.

From the orthopaedic point of[150] view, it was felt that his spine should be watched[160] carefully as he is likely to develop a kyphosis. Follow[170]-up has been arranged by Miss Sefton. It was felt[180] that his dislocated hips should be left untreated but that[190] his feet should be treated by strapping and stretching, with[200] the prospect of bilateral postero-medial releases.

It was thought[210] that a prognosis at this stage was difficult to make,[220] but it was noted that he had good upper limbs[230] and in time he may be able to walk with[240] a puil-through gait.

G Bates
14 January 19—   (*251 words*)

Note: Medical secretaries often assist doctors in their clinics by taking clinical notes. These clinics may be held in the same building as the doctor's office or even a considerable distance away, such as another hospital. This is because many doctors, particularly consultants, may work in several different medical locations.

Vocabulary

TCI (to come in)..................

Orthopaedic Clinic note for file (6 February 19— – same year as discharge):

Feet are improved, but the heels are still not down.[10] Needs bilateral postero-medial release. General condition good. Feeding well.[20] Kicks legs independently. Hips and knees are still both very[30] stiff. Combined adduction – 60 degrees. TCI soon for[40] bilateral postero-medial release.

G Bates   (*46 words*)

Vocabulary

capsulotomy..............., catgut..............., dorsiflexion..............., equinus...............,

eversion..............., facet..............., flexor digitorum communis (FDC)...............,

flexor hallucis longus (FHL)..............., GA (general anaesthetic)...............,

haemorrhage..............., mortice..............., os calcis..............., posterior-lateral. [shorthand], posterior tibialis. [shorthand],

sub talar. [shorthand], suturing. [shorthand], talus. [shorthand], tendo achilles. [shorthand],

tourniquet. [shorthand], varus. [shorthand], Z-lengthened. [shorthand]

OPERATION NOTES

SURNAME (block letters) ....FIRST NAME ....

DOB .... WARD Bluebell   HOSP REF .... DATE 2.3.19—

OPERATION Bilateral posterior-lateral release of the feet

SURGEON(S) Miss Sefton; Mr Bates

ANAESTHETIST(S) Mr Grace

PROCEDURE

Under GA there was significant varus and equinus[10] deformity of the feet. Posterior-lateral incision was made on[20] each side. The tendo achilles was Z-lengthened. Posterior tibialis[30] and flexor digitorum communis were divided. A full posterior capsulotomy[40] of the sub talar joints was carried out, taking particular[50] care to release the ligament on the lateral side. On[60] the medial side, the medial ligament of the ankle joint[70] was released as far forward as possible, as was the[80] sub talar joint. Following full release it was possible to[90] get the talus to come back into the ankle mortice.[100] It was clear that there was abnormal posterior lateral facet[110] on the talus where it had been lying against the[120] fibia. The extensive lateral release of the talus allowed this[130] to move back into its more normal position, and the[140] sub talar release allowed the os calcis to move to[150] externally rotate on the talus. Therefore, at the end of[160] the operation good correction of the foot was obtained into[170] dorsiflexion and eversion. Tourniquet off. On the left side there[180] was quite a lot of oozing but no major haemorrhage[190] could be identified. The wounds were closed in layers after[200] suturing the tendo achilles and the flexor hallucis longus with[210] catgut. Long leg plasters were applied and the knees flexed[220] as much as is possible. The foot position was very[230] satisfactory. He may still require a change of plaster shortly.[240] I suggest that he is re-admitted at 2 weeks for[250] assessment and probable change of plaster.

G Bates
3 March[260] 19—   (*263 words*)

Vocabulary

anatomy................., CDH (congenital dislocation of the hip). [shorthand],

haemostasis. [shorthand], CTEV (congenital talipes equinovarus)....... [shorthand],

Denis Browne boots. [shorthand], FLL (flexor lucis longus). [shorthand]

Summary (set out as summary on page 102), copies to paediatrician and GP:

DISCHARGE SUMMARY

ADMITTED: 1.3.19—   **DISCHARGED:** 22.3.19—

HISTORY

See previous summaries. Admitted on this occasion for surgery[10] to the feet. Had bilateral CTEV with significant[20] varus and equinus deformity in spite of stretching and strapping.[30]

OPERATION Bilateral posterior-lateral release – 2.3.19—[40]

SURGEON Miss Sefton

Under anaesthesia the significant varus and equinus[50] deformity was confirmed on both sides. A similar procedure was[60] carried out on both sides. Through postero-lateral incision the[70] tendo achilles was Z-lengthened. FLL was lengthened,[80] tibialis posterior and FDC were divided. A posterior[90] capsulotomy of the ankle and sub talar joints was carried[100] out extending as far forward as possible on both medial[110] and lateral sides. Following full release the talars would come[120] into the ankle mortice although the anatomy of the talus[130] was abnormal. A good correction of the heel was achieved.[140] Following haemostasis the skin was closed and bilateral long leg[150] plasters were applied. Two weeks later, change of plaster of[160] both feet.

OPERATION Change of plaster of both feet – 15.[170]3.19—

SURGEON Mr Bates

Under anaesthesia the[180] position remained excellent. Bilateral above knee plasters were re-applied in[190] full correction.

To be seen in 2 months for removal[200] of plasters and fit Denis Browne boots.

G Bates
18 March 19—   *(214 words)*

Vocabulary

fusion........................, scoliosis........................, strut graft........................,

XOA (X-ray on arrival)........................ .

Orthopaedic Clinic note (6 June 19—):

X-rays show approximately 20 degrees of scoliosis between T9[10] to L3. I think it might be worth considering[20] doing an anterior strut graft in spite of the disadvantage[30] in terms of growth. The curve in the upper lumbar[40] region is clearly abnormal and unlikely to be of full[50] potential anyway and a fusion will probably, therefore, have rather[60] less effect on the overall growth process. Query for fibular[70] strut graft. See in 4 months with XOA.[80]

J Sefton   *(82 words)*

Vocabulary

contractures...................., deteriorating..................., physiotherapy...................,

splints....................

From Consultant to GP (3 October 19—):

Dear Dr Webb

I have changed the Denis Browne boots[10] that this boy was wearing to back splints, which he[20] can now wear 24 hours a day. The Denis[30] Brownes were not entirely satisfactory as he was regularly able[40] to get his right foot free. On examination today his[50] hips and certainly his knees are slightly stiffer compared to[60] recent examination. His mother has been advised, therefore, to continue[70] physiotherapy at home to flex the knees and to reduce[80] the hip flexion contractures and also the adduction contractures.

I[90] am seeing Jamie again in 2 months' time and may[100] feel it necessary at that time, if the situation is[110] deteriorating, to request physiotherapy locally to stop his contractures from[120] progressing.

Yours sincerely

Jennifer Sefton   (*125 words*)

Vocabulary

distally...................., modifications...................., segment....................,

X-ray lateral (from one side to the other)...................., X-ray AP (anterior–posterior—

from front to back)....................

Orthopaedic Clinic note (5 December 19—):

Measured angle – 20 degrees with X-ray taken sitting, ie[10] no change. There appears to have been no change in[20] the clinical appearance or the X-ray. Clearly very abnormal segment[30] distally at T6. It looks as though the lower[40] spine is actually posterior to the upper lumbar with modifications.[50] Review in 6 months. XOA lateral and A[60]P.

D R Grace   (*64 words*)

Vocabulary

kyphus...................., thoracic...................., unilateral.....................

Orthopaedic Clinic note (22 May 19— – following year):

Thoracic lumbar curve is now 35 degrees but there[10] does not appear to have been any increase in the[20] kyphus. Spine is very stiff. In addition, his hips are[30] getting stiffer and there is only a small amount of[40] flexion on either side and, as such, he is totally[50] unable to sit. In view of the deterioration in the[60] back, query unilateral posterior fusion. He may also need some[70] sort of release of hips so that he will be[80] able to sit more correctly. To be reviewed in 3[90] months. TCI soon, name on waiting list.

G[100] Bates

(101 words)

Vocabulary

osteogenic........................, static...................

Memo from Senior Orthopaedic Registrar to Orthopaedic Surgeon (22 May 19—):

This young child with osteogenic scoliosis has deteriorated from 20[10] to 35 degrees, although his kyphus has remained static.[20] I have put his name on your waiting list for[30] unilateral posterior fusion. He is due to see you later[40] this year for assessment of his hips, knees and feet.[50] These are extremely stiff and I could not flex either[60] hip beyond 10 degrees today. I am uncertain what your[70] plan for his hips is and wondered whether you wanted[80] to do anything about them at the same time as[90] you were doing his back.

G Bates

(97 words)

Memo from Orthopaedic Surgeon to Senior Orthopaedic Registrar (2 June 19—):

Thank you for your memo and all your help with[10] Jamie. I think I had better review the hips when[20] he is in for spinal surgery. I am trying to[30] avoid involving him in hip surgery in the very near[40] future.

J Sefton

(43 words)

Patient admitted 16 December 19—. Orthopaedic Ward note:

Admitted for localised spinal fusion. Jamie is just 2 years[10] old now and his hips pose quite a problem as[20] they do not flex sufficiently to let him sit comfortably.[30] I am reluctant to consider excision of the hips at[40] this early stage. Probably the best thing to do is[50] to proceed with the fusion, see how he gets on[60] subsequently and, depending on how mobile he is, try to[70] avoid early hip surgery until it can be seen what[80] is going to be the best way for him to[90] get around.

J Sefton

(94 words)

Vocabulary

convexity...................., decorticated..................., iliac crests...................., thoraco-

lumbar...................., vertebrae..................... .

Summary (set out as summary on page 102), copies to Paediatrician and GP:

DISCHARGE SUMMARY

ADMITTED: 16.12.19—   **DISCHARGED:** 23.12.19—

HISTORY
See previous summaries. Jamie's thoraco-lumbar scoliosis is secondary[10] to the severe osteogenic

abnormalities in his lower thoracic spine[20] which, in the 5 months from December 19—[30] to May 19—, have increased from T9[40]–L3 20 degrees. His feet remained in good[50] position following his previous surgery. His hips are extremely stiff[60] and do not flex sufficiently to let him sit comfortably.[70]

OPERATION Unilateral posterior spinal fusion – 18.12.19—[80]

SURGEON Miss Sefton

The right side of the spine on[90] the convexity of the curve was approached. The anatomy of[100] the vertebrae was very abnormal. Available vertebral bone was decorticated[110] and bone graft from both posterior iliac crests applied over[120] the convexity of the curve.

He made an uneventful post[130]-operative recovery and was able to get home for Christmas.[140]

He has been fitted with a brace, which incorporates both[150] legs, and will be reviewed in the scoliosis clinic in[160] 2 months.

J Sefton
29 December 19—[170]

(*170 words*)

Vocabulary

2/12 (2 months' time)..*2/12*........ .

Scoliosis Clinic note (10 February 19—):

Wound healed well. X-ray shows no changes in curve. No[10] obvious sign of new bone formation. To continue in brace.[20] To be seen in 2/12. XOA.[30]

G Bates

(*32 words*)

WORKING WITH A PLASTIC SURGEON

Information

Consultant: Mr J Clarke FRCS   Epsom County Hospital   Epsom   Surrey KT18 7HW
Senior Plastic Surgery Registrar: Mr S O'Shea FRCS   Epsom County Hospital
General Practitioner: Dr R Robertson MB   36B Laurel Drive   Epsom   Surrey KT18 3QF
Patients: Mr Henry Smythe   12 Florence Way   Ashtead   Surrey KT17 3HU   DOB
    31.4.19—   Aged 62   *Hospital reference:* 374089/jc
Mrs Muriel Gresham   Highfield House   Selsdon Road   Leatherhead   Surrey KT18
    3HW   DOB 25.2.19—   Aged 59   *Hospital reference:* 389076/jc
Baby Amanda Massingham   238 Field Park Crescent   Fetcham   Surrey KT18
    2MW   DOB 25.12.19—   Aged 4 months   *Hospital reference:* 416782/jc

Vocabulary

grafting...*........*, tibia.................. .

From GP to Plastic Surgeon (re Mr Henry Smythe) (23 January 19—):

Dear Mr Clarke

I should be grateful if you would[10] see this patient who has a history of a chronic[20] ulcer on his right leg over the tibia. This has[30] been present for 12 years.

Apparently skin grafting has been[40] carried out twice in an attempt to cover the defect[50] but, as you will see, this has been unsuccessful. The[60] operations were performed at the hospital nearest to Mr Smythe's[70] old address – the Sheffield Infirmary. He is not on any[80] medication at present.

Yours sincerely

R Robertson

(87 words)

Vocabulary

full-thickness graft........., skin flap........., technique.........

From Consultant to GP (8 April 19—):

Dear Dr Robertson

Thank you for referring this patient on[10] whom I have arranged to do a skin flap (full[20]-thickness graft) as I think this technique will suit the[30] area better than his previous operations.

Examination showed that his[40] general medical condition was satisfactory and I will write again[50] after the operation.

Yours sincerely

J Clarke

(57 words)

Vocabulary

Amoxyl........., crepe bandage........., cross leg flap*.........,

devitalised........., excision........., granulate........., Jelonet.........,

Proteus.........

* Flap of skin from one leg to the other, legs strapped together. Skin flap remains joined until new blood supply is well-established, then legs are separated.

From Consultant to GP (12 September 19—):

Dear Dr Robertson

This patient of yours has had a[10] successful operation for excision of devitalised skin and bone from[20] his right leg and cross leg flap from the opposite[30] calf.

He was discharged home yesterday with a course of[40] oral Amoxyl 250 mg tds as[50] a wound swab showed a growth of Proteus. His legs[60] were dressed with Jelonet and crepe bandage applied. He was[70] anxious to go home even though a few small areas[80] on his legs were not quite healed but I am[90] sure that, given time, these areas will granulate nicely.

I[100] have asked him to attend the Out-patients Department in[110] one week's time but would appreciate you keeping an eye[120] on him in the meantime.

Yours sincerely

J Clarke   (*129 words*)

From GP to Consultant (17 September 19—):

Dear Mr Clarke

Mr Smythe attended my surgery today and[10] I am pleased to be able to report that his[20] legs seem to be healing satisfactorily.

He has now completed[30] his course of Amoxyl and is due to see you[40] in your Clinic in 2 days' time.

Yours sincerely

R[50] Robertson   (*51 words*)

Vocabulary

swab..ℰℒ.........., wound.↲............

From Consultant to GP (20 September 19—):

Dear Dr Robertson

I saw this gentleman in my Out[10]-patients Clinic yesterday and his legs appear well healed. A[20] further wound swab proved unnecessary as all areas have now[30] granulated. I have left the legs exposed and asked the[40] patient to put salt in his daily bath.

I shall[50] see him again for a final review in 4 weeks,[60] but I am sure that the flap will last him[70] the rest of his days.

With best wishes

J Clarke   (*80 words*)

From GP to Consultant (re Mrs Muriel Gresham) (4 March 19—):

Dear Mr Clarke

This lady has a lesion on the[10] top of her left ear and another at the corner[20] of her left eye. She says that they are not[30] painful but they are a source of embarrassment.

I would[40] welcome your suggestions regarding treatment or surgical removal.

Yours sincerely[50]

R Robertson   (*52 words*)

Vocabulary

basal cell carcinoma (BCC). ...., medial canthus ...., reconstruct ....

From Consultant to GP (1 May 19—):

Dear Dr Robertson

Thank you for referring this patient. She[10] has what appears to be a basal cell carcinoma below[20] the left medial canthus. I have suggested to Mrs Gresham[30] that I should excise this and reconstruct the defect with[40] a graft.

I am arranging for her to be admitted[50] for this and the lesion from her left ear will[60] be excised at the same time.

Kind regards

J Clarke

(70 words)

Vocabulary

actinic keratosis ...., cartilage ...., inner canthus ....,

post-auricular ...., primary ...., wedge ...., wolfe graft ....

Hospital summary, copy to GP.

SUMMARY OF IN-PATIENT TREATMENT AT EPSOM COUNTY HOSPITAL, EPSOM, SURREY

Consultant .... **Admitted** 20.9.19—

Department .... **Discharged** 26.9.19—

Patient's name ....

Address ....

....

DOB .... **Ref No** .... **Religion** ....

GP ....

DIAGNOSIS: 2 lesions on face

TREATMENT: excision and wolfe graft[10]

HISTORY: This 59-year-old woman was admitted routinely[20] for excision of 2 lesions—one close to the left[30] medial canthus and one on the left ear.

OPERATION: 2[40]1 September 19—, excision of lesions by Mr[50] O'Shea, Plastic Surgery Registrar. The lesion at the left medial[60] canthus was excised with a 3 mm margin. A wolfe[70] graft was taken from the post-auricular region. Wedge incision[80] of the lesion on the rim of the left ear,[90] including cartilage. Primary closure.

POST-OPERATION: Recovery was satisfactory and[100] on inspection at 5 days the take of the graft[110] was excellent.

HISTOLOGY: Inner canthus lesion showed an actinic keratosis.[120] Ear lesion showed a basal cell carcinoma. Both were completely[130] excised.

FOLLOW-UP: To be reviewed in Out-patients.

J[140] Clarke
22 September 19—   (*147 words*)

From Registrar in Plastic Surgery to GP (2 October 19—):

Dear Dr Robertson

I saw this patient of yours in[10] clinic today. Her wounds have settled satisfactorily and the sutures[20] have been removed today. I will see her again in[30] 3 months and, if all is well, with no sign[40] of recurrence, I will discharge her from the Clinic.

Yours[50] sincerely

S O'Shea   (*53 words*)

From GP to Consultant (re baby Amanda Massingham) (10 April 19—):

Dear Mr Clarke

On the advice of the Consultant Paediatrician[10] of our local hospital (Ashtead Memorial), where Amanda was born,[20] I am writing to ask you if you would kindly[30] take on this baby with a cleft palate.

With many[40] thanks

Yours sincerely

R Robertson   (*45 words*)

From Consultant to GP (29 May 19—):

Dear Dr Robertson

Thank you for asking me to see[10] this delightful baby with a large cleft of the soft[20] and hard palate but, I note, no lip involvement. I[30] have put her name on my waiting list to have[40] the cleft palate repaired when she is just under a[50] year old.

My Registrar had a long chat with the[60] parents and explained to them what would be involved and[70] that we hoped it would be just one operation, although[80] we would review her regularly in the Lip and Palate[90] Clinic.

Yours sincerely

J Clarke   (*95 words*)

Vocabulary

Amoxycillin............., Dexon............., Kilner-Wardile............., pyrexia.............

Epsom County Hospital Discharge Summary (set out as discharge summary on page 85) copy to GP:

Admitted 3.10.19—   **Discharged** 11.10.19—

DIAGNOSIS: cleft palate

TREATMENT: repair

HISTORY: This 10-month-old[10] baby girl was admitted for repair of the cleft palate.[20] It had been a normal pregnancy and there was no[30] family history of either cleft lip or palate. The baby[40] had some feeding difficulties but had been fitted with a[50] dental plate and was now bottle-feeding well.

EXAMINATION: She[60] had a cleft of the soft and hard palate, but[70] with no lip involvement.

OPERATION: 4 October 19—,[80] cleft palate repair by Mr Clarke. The procedure was a[90] modified Kilner-Wardile technique. Closure was with 4/0[100] Dexon.

POST-OPERATION: She developed a low-grade pyrexia and[110] was commenced on Amoxycillin.

FOLLOW-UP: To be reviewed in[120] Clinic.

J Clarke
14 October 19—   (*128 words*)

From Consultant to GP (25 October 19—):

Dear Dr Robertson

Mrs Massingham brought Mandy to have her[10] sutures removed today. The repair was very successful and will[20] entail, as I had hoped, only the one operation. I[30] will continue to review this baby routinely in the Clinic[40] over the next year.

Yours sincerely

J Clarke   (*48 words*)

6 Your Own List of Medical Words

Compose your own medical Teeline dictionary on the following pages.

__ABC__

<u>DEF</u>

<u>GHI</u>

<u>JKL</u>

MNO

PQR

<u>ST</u>

UVW

<u>XYZ</u>